Managing your woodland for wildlife

David Blakesley and Peter Buckley

Illustrated by
Tharada Blakesley

Sponsored by

– providing woods for enjoyment and conservation

piscespublications

Newbury, Berkshire

Citation
For bibliographic purposes, this book should be referred to as
Blakesley, D and Buckley, GP. 2016. *Managing your woodland for wildlife*. Pisces Publications, Newbury.

First published 2010.
Second edition 2016.

British-Library-in-Publication Data
A catalogue record for this book is available from the British Library.

ISBN: 978-1-874-35775-9

Pisces Publications is the imprint of
NatureBureau, 36 Kingfisher Court, Hambridge Road, Newbury, Berkshire RG14 5SJ
www.naturebureau.co.uk

Dr David Blakesley CEnv, MCIEEM (Wildlife Landscapes; Autism and Nature) is an ecological practitioner and writer, specialising in habitat restoration, wildlife surveys and engaging children with autism and related disabilities with the natural environment.
david.blakesley@autismandnature.org.uk
www.autismandnature.org.uk

Dr Peter Buckley MCIEEM is an ex-academic and forest ecologist, specialising in habitat restoration and management; peterbuckleyassociates@gmail.com

Disclaimer
The information presented in this book on behalf of the authors is believed to be accurate and correct, but this cannot be guaranteed. Readers must take all appropriate steps to ensure health and safety of all users, and to follow their own health and safety policy. The authors issue this book without responsibility for accidents or damage as a result of its use or the implementation of any of the recommendations within this book.

Printed by Henry Ling Limited, Dorchester

Cover photographs
Front cover: Common redstart (Markus Varesvuo / birdphoto.fi); white admiral and lady orchid (David Blakesley); dormouse (David Kjaer)
Back cover: Veteran beech (David Blakesley)

Contents

Foreword

Over the past 25 years, there has been an explosion in the number of people without much previous experience of woodlands who have become involved in caring for them. Many of you will be private owners. Our company has contributed to this change by making available a lot more small woodlands that can be managed by one individual, or a group of friends, or a family. Although there are many books on managing woodlands for timber production, there is far less about how you can actively encourage wildlife. This book has been commissioned to fill this gap. It is unashamedly aimed at those for whom the first priority is biodiversity and only secondarily the production of useful wood or timber products. Through the Small Woodlands Owners Group (SWOG) we are in touch with owners of all sorts of woods throughout Britain and we know that there is a hunger for this kind of knowledge.

New owners can be overwhelmed by the amount of advice they are given, and the apparent size of the task ahead. But take comfort. A forest floor littered with dead and rotting wood is not a sign of neglect – it reflects management aimed at benefitting a rich variety of deadwood insects and fungi, valuable in their own right, while providing shelter and nourishment for birds, small mammals, amphibians and reptiles. Elderly trees, with no further potential as timber, should not be cleared away but recognised as important sanctuaries for hole-nesting birds and roosting bats, as well as a diverse range of insects. An area of impenetrable scrub, including bramble, provides nesting sites and food for some of our declining woodland birds, and nectar for insects. A private clearing will provide an open area for a variety of sun-loving plants and butterflies. This also creates additional woodland edge, invaluable for many species.

Written by two well-known ecologists, this book caters specifically for owners and carers of woodlands, particularly small woodlands. It builds on and greatly amplifies the introductory account in *Getting started in your own wood* (Evans and Rolls, 2015) that many readers will be familiar with. The authors do not offer a prescription; rather, they describe types of woodland, how they function and develop naturally, sympathetic ways of managing the tree canopy, and the needs of various wildlife types. You may want to discuss your choices with professionals in the Forestry Commission or your local Wildlife Trust, both of whom we have found unfailingly helpful.

There is also a great deal of information and discussion on the internet. If you want to find people like yourself, and those with longer experience, you could browse the SWOG website (www.swog.org.uk). The Small Woods Association (SWA) website (www.swa.org) is another valuable resource, as is *Living Woods* Magazine (www.livingwoodsmagazine.co.uk).

At Woodlands.co.uk we take pride in the range of lively and informative blogs on our own website. Nearly four hundred of these are in the category of 'Flora and Fauna'. Like the authors, we believe that the owners and carers of woodlands have a major part to play in conserving and increasing future biodiversity in our countryside.

Margaret Hanton
Woodlands.co.uk

The entire text of this book is available on our website at www.woodlands.co.uk

Acknowledgements

We would like to begin by expressing our gratitude to Woodlands.co.uk for giving us the opportunity to write this book and subsequently to update the information contained within. Without their support and backing this book would not have been possible.

We are indebted to Professor Julian Evans (formerly Chief Research Officer for the Forestry Commission) and Margaret Hanton (Woodlands.co.uk) for providing constructive comments on the whole book. Many others have helped us by providing advice and information or by reviewing sections of text. We would especially like to thank Lee Brady (Kent Reptile and Amphibian group), Ruth Dalton (The Rare Breeds Survival Trust), Laura Dunne (Bat Conservation Trust), Dave Leech (British Trust for Ornithology), Colin Morris (Vincent Wildlife Trust), Tracy Pepler (Small Woodland Owners Group), Alan Rayner (University of Bath), Craig Shuttleworth (Red Squirrel Survival Trust), Nigel Symes (RSPB) and Penny Williams (Freshwater Habitats Trust). Any errors that remain are firmly our responsibility.

We would especially like to thank Tharada Blakesley for her inspired and detailed illustrations. Peter and Barbara Creed (Pisces Publications) made valuable suggestions on the design and layout of the book. Finally, we gratefully acknowledge the support and understanding of our families during the writing of this book.

David Blakesley and Peter Buckley
March 2016

Introduction

Despite the fact that Britain is one of the least wooded countries in Europe, woodland remains an important and dominant feature in the British landscape. It provides valuable habitat for wildlife and a wide range of benefits to society, including contributing to the economy; education; recreation; and health and well-being. All woodland in Britain has been shaped by human hands to some extent, whether it is ancient, semi-natural woodland dating back to medieval times, or recent in origin. Even in neglected woods, there are often clues to past management practices. For example, a densely stocked wood today might once have been managed as wood pasture, evident from the presence of old pollards; other woods might have been coppiced, with the remains of old coppice stools or standard oaks still present. In the 19th century, many ancient woods in South East England were converted to sweet chestnut coppice. More recently, large areas of ancient woodland across Britain have been converted to conifer or broadleaved plantations.

Most woodland management has been highly beneficial for wildlife over the centuries, creating many different habitats which have allowed a diverse flora and fauna to develop. These range from mature forest through to the temporary open areas created by coppicing and thinning, and the more permanent open space of rides and glades. Old-growth stands, ancient forests and wood pasture, developed over decades and centuries, are particularly

The endemic race of lesser spotted woodpecker is a rapidly declining woodland specialist, which may use isolated woods to navigate through otherwise 'hostile landscapes'.

important for specialist woodland species. The hollow, rotting limbs of veteran trees for example provide roosting and nesting opportunities for bats and birds; fallen deadwood provides a vital habitat for a diverse range of insects, fungi, lichens and mosses; and the species which feed on them. Other species rely heavily on coppicing; woodland specialist butterflies such as the small pearl-bordered fritillary thrive in newly coppiced areas, whilst some of our most threatened woodland birds such as nightingale and willow warbler breed in young coppice regrowth.

Sadly, the second part of the 20th century witnessed a period of management neglect which resulted in the reversion of large areas of coppice, under-thinned plantations and the loss of open space. As a consequence we have also seen a serious decline in woodland specialists, such as insects and birds, which rely heavily on scrub stages and young tree growth. Many have become species of conservation concern, designated as Priority Species i.e. species of principal importance (formerly known as UK Biodiversity Action Plan priority species) or in some cases, such as the dormouse, European Protected Species. Furthermore, climate change poses a new and serious threat for many woodland species. Most of us are aware of earlier bud burst, warmer summers, milder winters and an increase in the frequency of extreme weather events, but not all species are able to adapt to these changing circumstances. As woodland ecosystems respond and adapt to climate change, some species may need to re-locate to more suitable conditions elsewhere in Britain if they are to survive. Unfortunately, many are poor dispersers and will be unable to move. Others are more mobile, including some woodland insects and birds, but will face barriers in the landscape, such as large expanses of open land. Increasing habitat connectivity in the countryside will be critical to this process, and isolated woods, hedgerows, shelterbelts and shaws will have an important role to play in assisting the dispersal and colonisation that is likely to take place in future years; acting as corridors and stepping stones.

You may have been asked to manage a wood belonging to someone else, or be part of an organisation which has jointly taken on the care of a particular woodland. Or you may have a wood of your own, and perhaps only recently completed the purchase. In all of these cases, your primary motivation could be to conserve wildlife, or perhaps to use it for leisure and recreation, timber production or firewood. Small woodland ownerships mostly fall within the range of 2–10 hectares, but whatever the type of wood, its size and location, or the reasons behind its purchase, woodland owners and managers have an important opportunity to make a real contribution to the future of Britain's woodland wildlife.

This book aims to offer practical advice for understanding and managing small areas of woodland for wildlife. In the first chapter we describe different woodland types, and how to identify your own woodland. Chapter 2 helps you to become more familiar with the plants and animals in your wood. Whether or not you fell trees, cut coppice, clear undergrowth, conserve or destroy deadwood, can all have profound influences on the value of a wood for wildlife. In Chapter 3 we show ways in which you can actively manage your wood to improve the habitat for wildlife. Chapter 4 looks at the valuable habitat provided by woodland edges, permanent open spaces and deadwood. In Chapter 5 we consider additional ways in which you might try to encourage wildlife, from introducing wild flowers to putting up bat boxes. Such enhancement should enable you to choose ways to manage your wood which are appropriate to the kind of woodland you have, and your own abilities and aspirations. Chapter 6 considers the implications of climate change and how woods might help species to move through the landscape in the future. Above all, we hope that with a greater understanding of woodland biodiversity, you will get much more satisfaction and enjoyment from your woodland.

1 Identifying woodland types

1.1 Woodland origins in Britain

Over much of Britain woodland is the final, stable ecosystem, which is known as the 'climax' ecosystem. Following the last ice age, as the climate improved, trees migrated northwards from the parts of Southern Europe which escaped the ice, crossing the land bridge in what is now the southern North Sea, into Britain. Aspen, birch and sallow were followed by Scots pine, oaks, alder, limes and elms. Immigration continued until Britain was cut off by the flooding of the English Channel, around 8,000 years ago. Primary forest, the so-called 'wildwood', covered most of Britain at that time. Lime woods dominated southern Britain, with ash and elm abundant in woods in the west where soils were rich enough. Further north in Scotland, pine dominated the higher ground to the east, with Atlantic oak forests along the west coast. Major forest clearance began during the Neolithic period, as the wildwood was opened up by coppicing, the extraction of timber and clearances for agriculture. It is not known exactly when the wildwood disappeared, although by the early Iron Age probably about half had already been cleared in England, and little was left by the time of the Norman invasion.

Today, native woodland is often categorised as ancient or recent (secondary). Land which has remained wooded since medieval times at the latest (1600 AD), and possibly much earlier than this is termed ancient woodland. The Ancient Woodland Inventory (AWI) is a provisional guide to the location of ancient woodland in Britain that woodland owners are able to consult. In England, the AWI can be viewed on the Government's Magic map system as a map layer under 'Habitats' and 'Woodland'; in Wales and Scotland use the respective Forestry Commission map viewers. Some of these ancient woods are likely to be direct descendents of the original wildwood. In contrast, woods which developed on previously open ground from the start of the 17th century are termed recent or secondary woodland. Much of this recent woodland resulted from natural succession on abandoned heaths, moors and grassland. Ancient, and some recent woodland is often referred to as semi-natural, as it has been shaped by both man and nature. A third category refers to the deliberate planting of trees to create artificial plantations, usually for economic reasons. Plantations may be traced back to the 17th century, when they were predominantly broadleaved: sweet chestnut plantings in southern England arrived somewhat later, mostly during the 19th century (Rackham, 2003), replacing the previous coppice crops on former woodland sites. It was not until the end of the First World War that major planting programmes with conifers started. Some open habitats which would be protected today as country-level Priority Habitats i.e. habitats of principal importance (formerly known as UK Biodiversity Action Plan (BAP) priority habitats), including heaths, moors, grassland, bogs and sand dunes were systematically planted with a range of conifers, including Corsican pine, larch, Western hemlock, spruce and Scots pine. Even ancient woodland was felled to make way for plantations of conifers and sometimes broadleaved species, though as a policy this ceased by the mid-1980s. Thus, by the end of the 20th century conifers were the dominant forest type, accounting for more than half of British woodland. In the early 21st century policies have changed considerably, with most new planting being of broadleaves, and some plantations on ancient woodland sites (PAWS) now being replaced with native broadleaves or allowed to regenerate naturally. Woodland creation schemes now take into account habitat networks and the linking of ancient woods, and focus on issues such as the selection of trees and shrubs to accelerate the development of semi-natural ancient woodland types and their associated wildlife (Blakesley and Buckley, 2010).

1.2 Woodland succession and regeneration

Succession is essentially a series of more or less predictable changes in ecosystem structure and composition over time, which in Britain's temperate climate results in a relatively stable, mature woodland cover. Succession from bare rocks or sand dunes that have not previously supported plant communities is known as primary succession. Recent woodland regenerating on land which has previously supported plant communities, such as farmland, where a soil layer has already formed, is known as secondary succession. Britain's temperate climate usually leads to deciduous woodland, except in the Scottish Highlands, where Scots pine and juniper woodland can develop. Although the exact sequence of succession may vary with site, and in time, typical stages on ex-arable land in lowland Britain are summarised below:

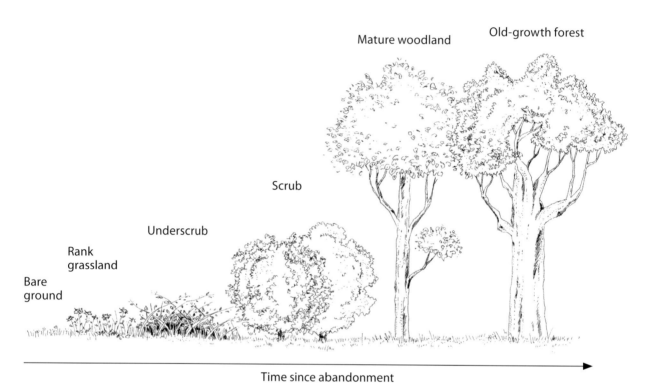

Example of a typical sequence of plant communities on ex-arable land, from bare ground through to old-growth forest.

Saplings of trees such as beech and ash may be found in the underscrub and scrub communities which develop dense thickets with closed canopies. The transition to oak woodland may follow, or on more base-rich brown earths, to ash woodland. Recognisable stages in the succession of the high forest include:

- maturing woodland with gaps in the canopy, allowing light to reach the woodland floor and trees and shrubs to regenerate
- mature woodland with little deadwood
- old-growth woodland with large trees, standing and fallen deadwood and younger, regenerating trees.

Each of these stages is distinct, both in terms of the structure of the wood, and the community of plants and animals which inhabit it. The timescale for secondary succession depends on factors such as the proximity of seed sources, soil conditions and competition from grasses and herbs. It can take many hundreds of years for recent woodland to closely resemble ancient woodland. Nevertheless, as a wood ages it becomes more diverse in many ways, and richer in wildlife. You may be able to recognise the stage of succession in your wood from the brief descriptions above.

Natural regeneration in mature woodland occurs when a gap is created by a falling tree, or rarely when a large number of trees are brought down by severe storms, such as occurred in the 1968 storm in Scotland and the 1987 storm in southern England. Regeneration in a tree fall gap may be compared to that in a newly coppiced or felled area. If a single tree falls, it creates opportunities for seedlings or root-suckers to develop from surrounding trees, particularly those which can thrive in partial shade such as beech. The fallen tree itself may sprout from the base and along the trunk, developing into a coppice-like thicket. When a larger gap is created by the collapse of several trees, more light reaches the woodland floor, enabling a wider range of trees and shrubs to establish themselves, mainly from seed. The amount of regeneration will vary, depending on distance from the 'new' woodland edge and the dispersal characteristics of seed from the mature trees present. Within the gap, some saplings and suppressed trees may already be present, ready to capitalise on the opening of the canopy. Others, such as pioneer willows and birch, with their light seeds will be early colonists; followed by the heavier seeds of trees such as oaks and hazel. This dynamic process often results in considerable structural diversity in the tree and shrub layer. Initially, the sudden increase in light will also have dramatic effects on the field layer, which may have been impoverished under the previous heavy shade. In ancient woodland, in the second season, the woodland floor may be carpeted with woodland flowers, augmented with herbs, grasses and rushes germinating from the soil seed bank. These include some light-demanding species whose seeds can survive for long periods in the soil, responding to the sudden increase in light. Eventually regenerating saplings close canopy, and the ground vegetation adjusts to the shady conditions once again.

When conifer plantations on ancient woodland sites (PAWS) are felled with the intention of allowing the site to regenerate naturally, the outcome is far more uncertain. Regeneration may follow a similar sequence of events, depending on the damage caused to the site during felling, and the extent to which the original flora and fauna survived in remnant patches of ancient woodland, often found along the margins of rides and forest roads, or the woodland perimeter. It is quite possible, however, that the tree cover will be provided by seedlings of the conifers, especially in the case of Scots pine or Western hemlock.

1.3 Identifying semi-natural woodland types

A greater understanding of your wood and its ecology will add to the pleasures of ownership and management. One of the first steps should be to identify the woodland vegetation type and, if possible, something of the underlying soils in your wood. This information would also guide the choice of species for any new planting within the boundaries of the wood, or on adjacent land. And if seed is sourced locally, from which woodland types it should be collected.

Woodland types are influenced by a range of factors, including climate, soils, geology and past management. In the uplands of Scotland, Wales and South West England, mild oceanic airstreams strongly influence the composition of woodland communities, the humid conditions particularly favouring rich woodland communities of ferns, mosses and lichens. In the central Highlands of Scotland, where winters are coldest, the pinewoods have some affinity with the forests of Scandinavia. Further south and east, English lowland woods experience wide temperature ranges, lower rainfall and frequent winter frosts. Oaks and ash dominate the canopy, with other trees and shrubs more frequent. In South East England, woods take on a more continental character, with beech and hornbeam being important components of the canopy.

Over the years, different authors have adopted different classification systems for British woodland. One of these, the National Vegetation Classification (NVC) (Rodwell, 1991), which deals with trees, shrubs and ground flora together, has become the most widely used system. A user-friendly key for identifying woodland NVC communities can be found in the *National Vegetation Classification: Field guide to woodland* (Hall *et al.*, 2004). More detailed information can be found in *British Plant Communities – Woodlands and scrub* (Rodwell, 1991). If you are competent at identifying trees, shrubs and prominent ground vegetation, and know the broad soil types, then the simplified key in Table 1.1 may help you to identify NVC types in your wood. The descriptions of different woodland types in Section 1.4 may also be helpful. You should initially divide your wood into visually different community types, with homogeneous areas within each type selected for identification purposes. Carry out surveys in the spring, from April to June, when most of the field layer plants are in flower.

Shrubby woodland edges, with a varied field layer and good structural diversity should also be surveyed, especially as such habitat is valuable for wildlife. A simple method is to survey 30 m lengths of woodland edge, identifying all the species present, if possible, assigning to each a visual cover percentage.

More detailed assessments of each community type can be undertaken based on the methods described in Hall *et al.*, (2004), with reference to keys given in Rodwell (1991).

1.4 Semi-natural woodland types

The following accounts are based on woodland habitats recognised as country-level Priority Habitats, showing their constituent woodland types described in the NVC (see Table 1.1).

A woodland owner examines the ground flora in an area of coppice to help identify the woodland type.

Lowland mixed deciduous woodland

This broad category includes ash and field maple woods (W8) and oak woods (W10, W16), which are associated with fertile soils, forming a continuum from base-rich to more acid soils. They tend to form mosaics with other types of woodland, particularly lowland beech and yew. Many have been converted to conifer plantations, or replaced with sweet chestnut or hornbeam coppice.

Ash-field maple woods tend to occur on soils that are not too acid (i.e. base-rich, neutral and even calcareous (limey) soils), although species other than ash, field maple and hazel may dominate, depending on the soil conditions. These include lime, hornbeam and oak in the canopy and blackthorn, elder, dogwood and spindle in the understorey. Identification of the dominant field layer species is usually necessary to identify the sub-community.

The lime-demanding species become less frequent on more acid soils, where pedunculate oak and birch are more prominent, although both species of oak may be present in oak-hornbeam woods (W10). Other prominent species include hornbeam, small-leaved lime and sweet chestnut, while ash is less frequent, particularly in South East England. Sub-communities characterised by wood anemone are frequent in South East England, while those with abundant ivy have a distinctly western bias.

On the impoverished acid soils of South East England, particularly on free-draining sandy plains, pedunculate oak and birch dominate (W16), other species are rarer, but may include rowan, alder, aspen and holly. The field layer is often dominated by bracken, wavy hair-grass and ericaceous species such as heather and bilberry, but is generally species-poor.

Lowland beech and yew woodland

Yew woodland (W13) occurs on steep, often south-facing chalk escarpments in southern England, and on the limestones of northern England, where it is usually associated with upland ash woods. Yew is the dominant canopy species, but may be accompanied by occasional ash, sycamore, pedunculate oak, whitebeam and beech.

The constant presence of beech in the canopy distinguishes three community types, that can tolerate soil conditions ranging from calcareous, neutral-basic to acid. Calcareous beech and yew woodland (W12) occurs mainly on chalk or limestone soils in South East England, within the natural range of beech, but also has a more restricted distribution in North West England. These woods are dominated by beech, whilst ash and sycamore are often present. Yew, holly and whitebeam are also characteristic, with pedunculate oak less common than in other beech wood types. The understorey may be sparse, but include a wide range of species.

Stands on neutral to slightly acidic and usually heavier soils can also be dominated by beech, with oaks being the most common associate (W14). The dense canopy results in a sparse field layer, with bramble the most common species. These beech woods often form mosaics or merge into typical oakwood communities (W10).

Acidic beech-wavy hair-grass woodland (W15) occurs on well drained sands and gravels. It has a much wider distribution than other beechwood types, but covers a smaller area. Oaks are the most common associate, with birches regenerating in gaps. Sycamore, wild cherry and whitebeam are scarce; and the shrub layer is usually poor or absent.

Wet woodlands

Wet woodlands occur on the seasonally waterlogged soils of floodplains, river valleys, and on fens, mires and bogs. Alder, birch and willows dominate, merging into oak, ash or beech communities in drier conditions, such as valley slopes. Willows dominate communities on the wettest sites, colonising the edges of standing open water, or in mires where succession is checked by a permanently high water table. In conservation terms, wet woods are important for their floristic variety and relict plant species of formerly open wetlands such as marsh fern; the deadwood habitats on wet substrates also support many localised invertebrates.

Table 1.1

NVC key to woodland types, based on **the key canopy species, ground flora component and broad soil types** (source: Forestry Commission, 2008; © Crown copyright, reproduced with the kind permission of the Forestry Commission).

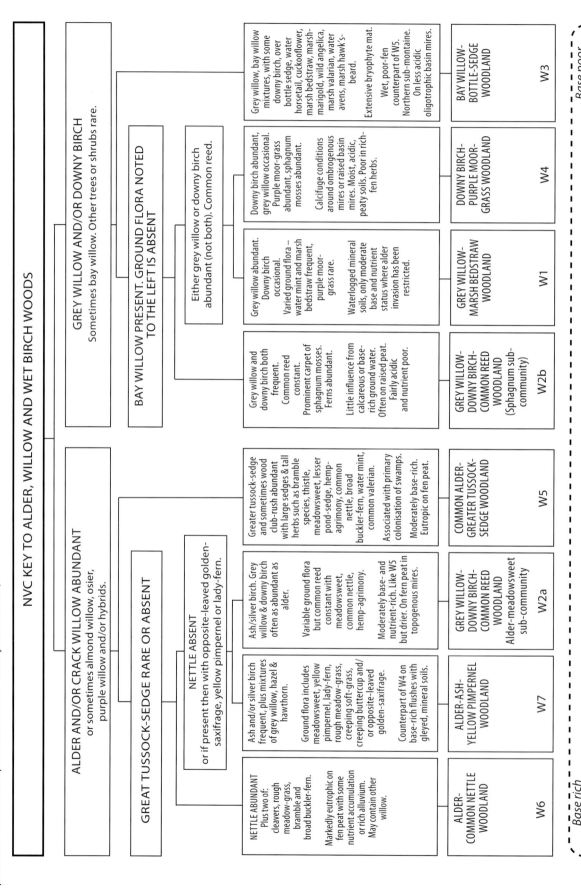

NVC KEY TO ALDER, WILLOW AND WET BIRCH WOODS

ALDER AND/OR CRACK WILLOW ABUNDANT
or sometimes almond willow, osier, purple willow and/or hybrids.

GREAT TUSSOCK-SEDGE RARE OR ABSENT

NETTLE ABSENT
or if present then with opposite-leaved golden-saxifrage, yellow pimpernel or lady-fern.

NETTLE ABUNDANT Plus two of: cleavers, rough meadow-grass, bramble and broad buckler-fern. Markedly eutrophic on fen peat with some nutrient accumulation or rich alluvium. May contain other willow.	Ash and/or silver birch frequent, plus mixtures of grey willow, hazel & hawthorn. Ground flora includes meadowsweet, yellow pimpernel, lady-fern, rough meadow-grass, creeping soft-grass, creeping buttercup and/or opposite-leaved golden-saxifrage. Counterpart of W4 on base-rich flushes with gleyed, mineral soils.

ALDER- COMMON NETTLE WOODLAND	ALDER-ASH- YELLOW PIMPERNEL WOODLAND
W6	W7

Greater tussock-sedge and sometimes wood club-rush abundant with large sedges & tall herbs such as bramble species, thistle, meadowsweet, lesser pond-sedge, hemp-agrimony, common nettle, broad buckler-fern, water mint, common valerian. Associated with primary colonisation of swamps. Moderately base-rich. Eutropic on fen peat.

COMMON ALDER- GREATER TUSSOCK- SEDGE WOODLAND

W5

GREY WILLOW AND/OR DOWNY BIRCH
Sometimes bay willow. Other trees or shrubs rare.

BAY WILLOW PRESENT. GROUND FLORA NOTED TO THE LEFT IS ABSENT

Either grey willow or downy birch abundant (not both). Common reed.

Grey willow and downy birch both frequent. Common reed constant. Prominent carpet of sphagnum mosses. Ferns abundant. Little influence from calcareous or base-rich ground water. Often on raised peat. Fairly acidic and nutrient poor.	Grey willow abundant. Downy birch occasional. Varied ground flora – water mint and marsh bedstraw frequent, purple moor-grass rare. Waterlogged mineral soils, only moderate base and nutrient status where alder invasion has been restricted.

GREY WILLOW- DOWNY BIRCH- COMMON REED WOODLAND (Sphagnum sub-community)	GREY WILLOW- MARSH BEDSTRAW WOODLAND
W2b	W1

Grey willow, downy birch often as abundant as alder. Variable ground flora but common reed constant with meadowsweet, common nettle, hemp-agrimony. Moderately base- and nutrient-rich. Like W5 but drier. On fern peat in topogenous mires.	Downy birch abundant, grey willow occasional. Purple moor-grass abundant, sphagnum mosses abundant. Calcifuge conditions around ombrogenous mires or raised basin mires. Moist, acidic, peaty soils. Poor in rich-fen herbs.

GREY WILLOW- DOWNY BIRCH- COMMON REED WOODLAND Alder-meadowsweet sub-community	DOWNY BIRCH- PURPLE MOOR- GRASS WOODLAND
W2a	W4

Grey willow, bay willow mixtures, with some downy birch, over bottle sedge, water horsetail, cuckooflower, marsh bedstraw, marsh-marigold, wild angelica, marsh valarian, water avens, marsh hawk's-beard. Extensive bryophyte mat. Wet, poor-fen counterpart of W5. Northern sub-montaine. On less acidic oligotrophic basin mires.

BAY WILLOW- BOTTLE-SEDGE WOODLAND

W3

Base rich
Nutrient rich

Base poor
Nutrient poor

Table 1.1 continued

NVC KEY TO WOODS WHERE ALDER AND WILLOW ARE NOT PROMINENT IN THE CANOPY

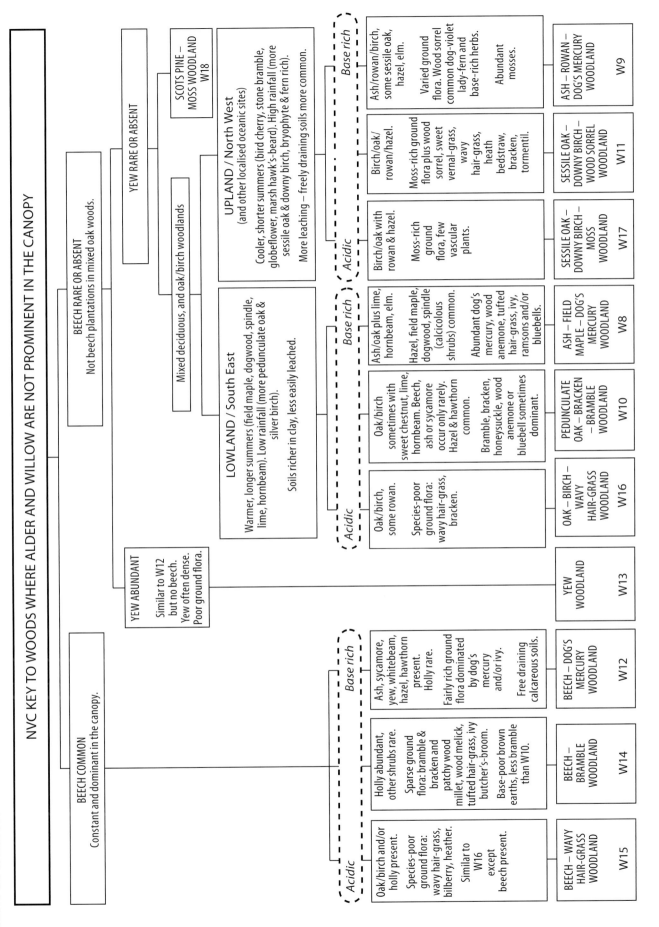

Grey willow with marsh bedstraw woodland (W1) occurs mainly on mineral soils along the margins of water, often as a narrow fringe, and has a somewhat western, coastal distribution. Grey willow with downy birch woodland (W2) develops on fen peat and terraces of river valley mires, especially in East Anglia. Common reed is usually present, as a relic of preceding fen communities. A third type, bay willow with bottle sedge woodland (W3) is a community of peat soils, restricted to northern Britain. Grey willow may also dominate this woodland, with occasional downy birch, but alder is rare.

On more fertile, base-rich soils, alder dominates wet woodland communities. Alder with greater tussock-sedge woodland (W5) predominates on organic fen peats, but where there is an accumulation of alluvium a nettle understorey (W6) can develop, with associates in its various sub-communities of grey or crack willow and downy birch. On less fertile, predominantly mineral soils where there is little peat accumulation, the characteristic community changes to alder with ash and yellow pimpernel woodland (W7). This community is most extensive in the wetter parts of Britain. Alder is often dominant, but ash can be frequent, together with sycamore and sessile oak.

A further type of wet or bog woodland, downy birch with purple moor-grass (W4c) can develop in moderately acidic conditions on deep peats from wet heath and mires. Grey willow and alder occasionally occur in woodland dominated by downy birch. Sphagnum mosses are prominent in the field layer, which tends to be species poor,

Upland birch woods
Communities of downy birch and purple moor-grass (W4) are also known as upland birch woods, forming part of the continuum between upland oak woods and open moorland. On the poorer, moderately acidic peaty soils, birches become dominant at the expense of oak with occasional rowan, willows, juniper and aspen. The understorey is generally sparse. Sub-communities of this type on drier sites are characterised by species such as broad buckler-fern and bramble (W4a), with soft rush (W4b) and sphagnum mosses (W4c) becoming progressively frequent on wetter and peaty sites. At the interface with the upland oak communities, the field layers often consist of heather and bilberry, giving way to bracken and wavy hair-grass on richer soils.

Upland oak woods
Upland oak wood communities have a western, Atlantic distribution from the South West peninsula to northern Scotland. The oceanic influence is responsible for the prominence of sub-Atlantic species such as holly, honeysuckle, climbing fumitory and heath bedstraw, as well as a very rich flora of mosses, ferns and lichens. Most upland oak woods occur on relatively poor, acid soils, where high rainfall often leads to strong leaching. Both pedunculate and sessile oak may be present, with downy and silver birch, and less frequent rowan and hazel. The shrub layer is often poorly developed. Grasses are frequent in the field layer, and herbs such as bluebell and wood anemone are present, the latter being commoner in more 'continental' sub-communities in North East Scotland. On the thinnest soils and most exposed sites, birch predominates over a heathy vegetation.

Three related communities have ground floras characterised by wood sorrel (W11), wavy hair-grass (sub-community W16b) and greater fork-moss (W17). The upland fringe of a variant of lowland oak-bracken-bramble woods (W10e), can be difficult to distinguish from sessile oak woodland (W11) as sessile oak tends to dominate, usually accompanied by sycamore, ash and wych elm. Hornbeam is absent or very rare. The field layer can be relatively rich, with wood sorrel and common dog-violet.

Upland mixed ash woods
The main community, ash with rowan and dog's-mercury (W9) replaces the lowland ash woods (W8) in northern Britain, upland Wales and Scotland where suitable calcareous substrates occur. Three W8 sub-communities, containing abundant herb Robert, ramsons

and wood sage respectively, are also upland types. The cooler, wetter conditions allow a greater development and variety of ferns and bryophytes in the field layer, but under heavy grazing a grassy sward develops. Ash and hazel are the dominant canopy species, with frequent rowan, downy birch and occasional oak, elm and sycamore, and a distinct shrub layer. The field layer can be very species-rich if grazing pressures are low, with characteristic species such as wood sorrel, violets, dog's-mercury, bluebell and herb Robert.

Native pinewoods

The Caledonian pinewoods (W18) of the central and north western Highlands of Scotland and are best developed on acidic, strongly leached soils, usually with thick organic surface layers. Scots pine is the dominant tree, although its distribution is often discontinuous and patchy in older or damaged stands. It is accompanied by occasional birches, rowan and juniper. Field layers are rich in mosses and ericaceous species such as heather, bilberry and cowberry, with the proportion of mosses and purple moor-grass increasing in the wetter, western stands. In very wet areas, pine tends to grow poorly and is replaced by downy birch, creating a mosaic of the wetter upland birch wood sub-communities (W4b and W4c) among pine stands. Wavy hair-grass is abundant in stands heavily grazed by deer and sheep. Impoverished versions of the main vegetation type may also be found in plantations of conifers in south western Scotland and Cumbria.

Wood pasture and parkland

Wood pasture and parkland is the final woodland habitat recognised as a country-level Priority Habitat, found in managed medieval wood pastures or commons, or as pre-19th century landscape parks. Most are found in the lowlands, but wood pasture is also widely distributed in the Scottish uplands. They are characterised by large, open-grown and often pollarded trees, scattered over a matrix of unimproved, grazed grasslands or heathlands. These veteran trees provide valuable habitats in their own right, often supporting distinctive epiphytic lichens and mosses, together with fungi and invertebrates which live in rotten wood, water-filled cavities on live trees, and sap runs. A range of woodland communities may be represented, typically those of lowland beech and yew (W14, W15) and mixed deciduous woodland (W10, W16); together with the corresponding open ground habitats.

Wood pasture has undergone many changes in recent centuries, which can hinder its recognition. Precious habitat has been lost to afforestation with exotic conifers; some has been converted to pasture with veteran trees restricted to field margins, or incorporated into parkland and golf courses; whilst other wood pasture has been underplanted with trees, or allowed to develop into closed canopy woodland. If you are unsure whether a wood was formerly wood pasture, the presence of veteran, open grown trees in a wood is a strong clue to suggest it was formerly managed as open, grazed woodland, particularly if the trees have been pollarded. Further evidence might be found by checking first edition Ordnance Survey maps from the mid 19th century, as these recorded open woodland with distinct scattered tree symbols.

Scrub communities

Some types of scrub represent stages in succession from open ground to woodland, whilst others are more stable, representing an important habitat in their own right. If you have areas of scrub, it is important to remember that the conservation value of scrub is very high, and hence it should be protected if possible. The NVC recognises five scrub types and two under-scrub communities. The most common types in lowland Britain are hawthorn with ivy (W21), blackthorn with bramble (W22) and bramble with Yorkshire-fog (W24); the latter often develops into hawthorn-ivy scrub on neutral or base-rich soils, and to gorse-bramble scrub (W23) on acid soils. Blackthorn scrub tends to dominate deeper, moist and richer neutral soils. A mosaic may develop with patches of hawthorn and blackthorn scrub, interspersed with bramble-Yorkshire-fog. In the mountains of northern Britain, juniper

Ancient hornbeam pollard.

heath (W19) occurs in the eastern and central Scottish Highlands and in more isolated stands on hills south to the Lake District; while high-altitude stands of dwarf willows, such as downy willow (W20), are located mainly in the southern and central Highlands of Scotland.

Plantations on ancient woodland sites

If you own an area of ancient woodland which has been replanted with conifers, or broadleaves such as sweet chestnut or beech, you may wish to know more about the woodland that formerly occupied the site. Some of the original vegetation may remain along the margins of conifer plantations, whilst woodland herbs may thrive in broadleaved woodland plantations. Together with information on soils, this vegetation may give strong clues to the original woodland types. Local 'reference sites' on similar soil types could be visited to establish what ancient woodland communities naturally occur, and if woodland restoration is being considered, these sites can inform species choice.

Recent woodland

The majority of woodland in Britain is 'recent' in origin (i.e. post 1600), resulting from secondary succession on cleared land such as lowland arable farmland, or deliberate planting. Some of the older woods which have come about through the scrubbing over of abandoned moors, heaths and grassland are classified as semi-natural, because they have assumed a mature woodland character, with some of the features of interest found in ancient woods. In contrast, younger regenerated woods do not usually match the species richness of ancient woodland. Small woodlands planted on less productive farmland in lowland England in the past 50 years or so also frequently fail to match any NVC type. They may suffer from poor structural diversity and possess a ground flora characterised by common shade-tolerant plants with efficient dispersal mechanisms (see Section 2.1). If your wood falls into these categories, methods for enriching their structural diversity, and their tree, shrub and ground flora communities are discussed in Chapters 3 and 4.

2 Learning more about your woodland and its wildlife

Before embarking on a programme of woodland management, it is useful to find out as much about the wildlife in your wood as possible. It is especially important to recognise whether any European Protected Species or other species of conservation concern are present and to help protect them if any management operations are undertaken. If your wood is part of a much larger block of woodland, it would also be worthwhile learning something about the wildlife in the woodland as a whole, so permission may be required to enter these areas. Whilst it is entirely possible to devise a conservation management plan based on a single compartment, it is much better if this takes account of the whole wood, and even better if the management of other compartments can be coordinated with other woodland owners.

Learning about the wildlife living in your wood can be a particularly enjoyable experience, especially if you are involved in surveys yourself. In the following accounts we introduce different groups of woodland flora and fauna, including some guidance on survey methods which might be used to learn more about your wood. Many of these methods are derived from more sophisticated survey techniques that are described more fully in other publications. Depending on your experience, you should be able to undertake some surveys yourself, although others may require specialist assistance, or may not be necessary for your wood. When it comes to identifying difficult groups such as lichens, the decision to survey your wood really depends on your own curiosity and motivation. In some areas, you may find that local specialist wildlife groups might be willing to undertake a survey for you for no charge, particularly if there may be species of conservation concern present. On the west coast of Scotland for example, where oak woods are rich in epiphytic lichens and mosses, you may have little problem in persuading local lichenologists to carry out a survey. In lowland Britain, local bat groups may be keen to survey mature woods where specialist woodland bats might occur.

2.1 Woodland plants

The sites of ancient woods have been continuously wooded since medieval times (pre-dating 1600 AD), and in rare cases may even be survivors of the wildwood itself, although all will have been managed and modified at different times. Despite this interference, it is possible that the plant communities of the ancient woodland floor may have changed little in that time, and may therefore be considered as essentially semi-natural. Plants that typify ancient woodland are not normally found in other habitats, although some may survive woodland clearance and persist in hedgerows marking the original woodland edge. It is the general characteristics of most ancient woodland plants which restrict them to this habitat. These include poor dispersal mechanisms; production of few seeds that do not remain viable in the seed bank; a reliance on vegetative propagation; and limited competitive ability.

These ancient woodland plants are sometimes referred to as ancient woodland 'indicator' species (Table 2.1) and are used by ecologists to ascertain whether a wood is likely to be ancient or more recent. It is relatively easy for you to investigate the history of your wood in this way. However, some care is needed because not all ancient woodland plants are restricted to ancient woodland and some that are good indicators in one region may be more widely distributed in others. For example, marsh violet and golden-rod are classed as indicator plants in South East England, but not in East Anglia. Hedge woundwort and herb Robert are indicators of ancient woodland in Scotland, although they are cosmopolitan species south of the border. A final important point is that the presence of a small number of ancient woodland plants is not a reliable indication of the age of a wood. If more species are present, this increases confidence that one is looking at ancient woodland, although there are no specific rules or limits. Other historical evidence may also be used to identify ancient woodland, such as the presence of wood banks and pollards.

Table 2.1
Examples of plants that are most strongly associated with ancient woods in Britain.

Bird's-nest orchid	Hay-scented buckler-fern	Sweet woodruff
Butcher's-broom	Herb Paris	Toothwort
Columbine	Lily-of-the-valley	Wild service-tree
Cow-wheat	Midland hawthorn	Wood goldilocks
Crab apple	Moschatel	Wood meadow-grass
Early dog-violet	Nettle-leaved bellflower	Wood melick
Hairy woodrush	Sanicle	Wood sedge

Some plants are tolerant of a range of soil types and are widespread in ancient woodland whereas others have quite specific requirements for soil conditions and shade. For example, bracken, creeping soft-grass, wavy hair-grass and marsh violet are found on acid woodland soils; oxlip, lady orchid and early dog-violet on basic soils. Bluebell and wood anemone are primarily plants of mildly acid conditions, but will tolerate a wide range of pH; similarly, dog's-mercury is a plant of calcareous soils which is also pH-tolerant.

Because soil type and soil conditions vary, it is not unusual to find many different plant communities within a single wood. For example, if you own a wood in southern England situated predominantly on chalk downland, it may extend onto deposits of clay drift, while further variation in soil conditions might be brought about by even slight changes in slope and drainage. The woodland ground flora on the chalky soils may be dominated by dog's-mercury, with species such as yellow archangel and nettle-leaved bellflower, but on areas of clay drift these may be replaced by bluebell, wavy hair-grass and hard fern. This example also

Midland hawthorn has a strong affinity for ancient woodland, it can be distinguished from hawthorn by the leaf shape (see inset, not to scale), although hybrids do occur.

illustrates the fact that most woodland communities are dominated by one, or a few species, such as bluebell or dog's-mercury, whose structure influences the diversity and abundance of other species.

Very few woodland plants actually require shade and could more properly be classed as shade-evaders, leafing and flowering in the spring before the leafy canopy develops. Others which grow or persist when trees are in leaf are better classed as shade-tolerant. Some species such as wood vetch prefer the partial shade of woodland margins, whilst others, such as bluebell and pignut, are found both under the woodland canopy and in open grassland.

Plant communities in the woodland field layer also include species which are more mobile and therefore characteristic of more recent as well as ancient woodland. These species have highly effective dispersal mechanisms and in some cases also the ability to compete on more fertile soils. They include species such as black bryony, enchanter's-nightshade, sweet violet and lords-and-ladies (Table 2.2). Many other species, including those tolerant of partial shade and sun, are more likely to persist in the woodland seed bank.

Table 2.2
Woodland shade-tolerant plants with more efficient dispersal mechanisms which are often found in more recent woodland.

Black bryony	False brome	Male-fern
Bramble	Giant fescue	Narrow buckler-fern
Broad buckler-fern	Ground ivy	Raspberry
Broad-leaved willowherb	Hairy-brome	Red campion
Common gromwell	Hedge woundwort	Sanicle
Common nettle	Herb Robert	Sweet violet
Common twayblade	Honeysuckle	Three-nerved sandwort
Dewberry	Ivy	Wood avens
Enchanter's-nightshade	Lords-and-ladies	Wood dock

The common twayblade is an orchid which may be found in more recent woodland.

Other woodland plants are more characteristic of the woodland edge, and thrive in both partial shade and full sunlight. These include species such as cleavers, cow parsley, ground elder and nipplewort.

Plants of woodland rides and glades

How much open space is desirable in a wood? As a precedent, the amount present in the original 'wildwood' is a topic which is frequently discussed. Views often polarise towards one of two theories; that the wildwood contained large areas of open space, which may have been maintained by grazing herbivores; or that the wildwood was essentially a closed canopy forest, with smaller open areas associated with tree-fall gaps, for example. The true picture may lie somewhere in between, but this is not a topic which we will discuss in detail here. In more recent times, it is also difficult to quantify woodland open space, as it has rarely been recorded in the historical record. Rackham (1990) suggests that most woodland rides are likely to be post-medieval, and that woodland open spaces were used for sport and grazing.

Today rides, glades and woodland perimeters are very important components of mature woodland habitat (Section 4.1), particularly if they have a long history. More woodland herbs and grasses are likely to be associated with these areas than in the high forest itself. Open ground communities may be diverse, closely resembling species-rich grassland, heathland or marshy areas, although rarer species characteristic of these habitats may be absent. Species such as meadow buttercup, meadowsweet and tormentil are just as likely to be encountered in ancient woodland rides as in open grassland. Consequently, the importance of rides and glades in conservation terms should not be underestimated, and in some parts of Britain, some of the best examples of semi-natural grassland are to be found in ancient woodland rides.

Owner learning to identify woodland plants.

Survey methods

A lot can be learnt about the ground flora in your wood by identifying and recording flowering herbs and grasses through the spring and summer months, with the aid of a good field guide such as *The Wildflower Key* (Rose, 2006). Alternatively, woodland plants may be surveyed more formally using replicated quadrats placed in homogeneous areas of vegetation. In each quadrat, the species present and their cover should be recorded, noting any other species present in the environs. Surveys of the shade-tolerant plants of high forest or coppice woodland should be undertaken in spring, following the method of Hall *et al.* (2004). For rides and glades, surveys are best undertaken in mid-summer, when the majority of grasses and herbs are flowering. Homogeneous areas should again be selected, and surveys should be repeated if different communities are present, for example if heathland and grassland are present in different parts of the wood. The *National Vegetation Classification users' handbook* (JNCC, 2006) also provides details of the methodology for sampling and describing vegetation communities. Refer to the keys given in Rodwell (1991 *et seq*) to determine the most appropriate NVC community classification. Computer programs can be used to calculate the 'goodness of fit' of data collected from quadrats to the expected species composition of semi-natural woodland communities and sub-communities recognised by the NVC. One such program, 'Tablefit' (Hill, 1996), is available freely from the Centre for Hydrology and Ecology, as is another in the MAVIS (Modular Analysis of Vegetation Information) software (Centre for Ecology and Hydrology, 2010).

2.2 Woodland insects

Old-growth ancient woodland supports more insects than any other habitat in Britain. This is due partly to its complex structure, resulting from the presence of 'old' trees, trees of different heights and ages, abundant deadwood on the ground, gaps in the high canopy, shrubby woodland margins and open sunny areas. Collectively, these habitats contain a large number of habitat niches for insects, including the following examples:

- living wood supports wood borers
- decaying wood on living trees, including damaged bark and roots support a diverse range of specialist insects
- fallen deadwood supports a specialist insect fauna
- fungi, soil, leaf litter and seepages in the ground support specialist insect faunas respectively
- bark is used for cover and by predators
- sap runs support specialist beetles and flies
- foliage of trees and shrubs is used by a very wide range of insect larvae
- flowers provide nectar
- gall-causing insects use roots
- climbers such as ivy provide food, cover and niches for hibernation
- mosses and liverworts provide cover.

Most insect families are represented in British woodland, some by a very large number of species; for example over 300 moth species can be found in an old oak wood. Trees and shrubs are particularly attractive to insects, but the number of species they can support varies enormously; top of the list are the willows, birches and oaks, each group known to support well over 400 insect species, many of which feed exclusively on the host tree. Other species such as blackthorn, hawthorn and alder also support a rich diversity of insects, although it is important to point out that not every individual tree or shrub, or small population will support all the insects known to use that species. At the other end of the spectrum elms, honeysuckle and yew support few insects, but they are still important components of a woodland community, because each hosts insects which feed exclusively upon them. Predatory and parasitic insects are also dependent on woodland plants, for the herbivorous insects upon which they prey.

Rich assemblages of insects in old-growth woodland usually only survive where the habitat has benefitted from historical continuity of management. Many species are highly specialised, occupying particular habitat niches, which may vary with the insect's growth stage. Sadly, rich assemblages of woodland insects are now scarce, due to in part the loss of native woodland, inappropriate management, conversion to chestnut coppice or conifers, and more recently to neglect.

Although there are many specialist habitat niches for insects in high forest; coppiced areas, shrubby woodland margins and open spaces in your wood are also important for insects and their predators. Insects make extensive use of shrubs, particularly dense clumps of bramble in sunny positions, patches of tall herbs and short turf, as the following examples illustrate:

- some insects are associated with lichens, algae and fungi growing on the bark of shrubs
- froghoppers and leafhoppers feed on plant sap
- a diverse range of insect larvae, such as moths, feed on leaves
- bumblebees and many other insect families feed on pollen and nectar
- purple emperor butterflies feed on aphid honeydew
- dragonflies and ants hunt along the woodland edge
- spiders use the vegetation to support webs
- leaf-cutter bees construct nests
- stem-nesting solitary wasps utilise bramble
- many insects including butterflies find shelter along the woodland edge
- a diverse range of adult insects bask on sunny woodland margins
- spiders hunt on bare ground.

Many insects which spend their larval stages in the damp shady conditions of the high forest, as adults require good quality woodland edge for basking and nectaring. Others may be associated with species-rich grasslands, but with the destruction of so much of this habitat,

The argent and sable is a day-flying moth found in woodland open areas, easily recognised by its distinctive black and white pattern.

woodland open spaces may provide a refuge. Generalists, found in a wide range of habitat such as hedgerows, parks and gardens also use woodland margins and open spaces. When planning work in your woodland, it is important to bear in mind the value of these various habitats.

One of the few insect families which are relatively easy for you to observe and identify are butterflies. As well as being one of the most charismatic groups of woodland insects, butterflies are also widely recognised as indicators of ecosystem health. Surprisingly, the majority of butterflies found along woodland margins, and in sunny rides and glades are actually classified as 'wider countryside species' (Table 2.3). Wider countryside species are so called because they utilise habitat which is still widespread in the countryside, and many are relatively mobile. Some breed in colonies, and may therefore be resident in a wood. Others are more opportunistic, ranging widely across the landscape, breeding wherever suitable habitat presents itself. Despite these characteristics, many widespread species have declined considerably in both abundance and occurrence over the past four decades, such as the white-letter hairstreak and small heath (Fox *et al.*, 2015).

A second group of butterflies are classified as 'habitat specialists', as they require specific habitat types which tend to be localised and isolated, such as coppiced woodland or species-rich grassland (Table 2.4). These butterflies are relatively sedentary, and the larvae of most feed on just one or two foodplants. Most have suffered major range and/or population declines; they are present on one or more of the country Priority Species lists i.e. species of principal importance (formerly known as UK Biodiversity Action Plan (BAP) priority species) and included on the UK butterfly Red-list as a result.

Many habitat specialists which breed in woodland are also found in other habitats in the vicinity, including scrub, hedgerows, grassland or heathland. Others utilise different habitats in different parts of the country. Heath fritillary for example occurs in woodland open spaces in South East England but occupies sheltered heathland combes in the South West. Only wood white, black hairstreak, white admiral and silver-washed fritillary are predominantly woodland specialists.

Table 2.3
Wider countryside butterflies found in woodland habitats.

Small skipper	White-letter hairstreak [1,2]	Comma
Essex skipper	Small copper	Speckled wood
Large skipper	Brown argus	Scotch argus
Brimstone	Common blue	Marbled white
Large white	Holly blue	Gatekeeper
Small white	Red admiral	Meadow brown
Green-veined white	Painted lady	Ringlet
Orange tip	Small tortoiseshell	Small heath [1,2]
Purple hairstreak	Peacock	

[1] Country-level Priority Species; [2] Red-listed species (Fox *et al.*, 2010)

Table 2.4
Habitat specialist butterflies found in woodland habitats.

Chequered skipper [1,2]	Brown hairstreak [1,2]	Small pearl-bordered fritillary [1,2]
Dingy skipper [1,2]	Black hairstreak [2]	Pearl-bordered fritillary [1,2]
Grizzled skipper [1,2]	Duke of Burgundy [1,2]	High brown fritillary [1,2]
Wood white [1,2]	White admiral [1,2]	Silver-washed fritillary
Green hairstreak	Purple emperor [2]	Heath fritillary [1,2]

[1] Country-level Priority Species; [2] Red-listed species (Fox *et al.*, 2010)

The white admiral is a woodland specialist butterfly, here basking on elm leaves.

In woodlands, the majority of habitat specialists require woodland edge habitat, sunny rides and glades, or areas recently coppiced or clear-felled. The decline of many species has resulted from the abandonment of traditional management practices such as coppicing over the past 100 years or so, which has resulted in severely shaded conditions. Habitat specialists have quite specific microhabitat requirements which are easily disturbed or destroyed, and once a species is lost from an area, there is often little prospect of recolonisation, due to the sedentary nature of these butterflies and woodland fragmentation. Reintroduction programmes may therefore be the only prospect for some species. Pearl-bordered fritillary for example is now being reintroduced at a private woodland in the Rother Woods. If Butterfly Conservation, a national voluntary organisation, has a re-introduction project near your wood, they may be interested to involve you in it. Contact them through their website.

Survey methods

With the exception of butterflies, insect identification is a specialist area, beyond the expertise of many amateur naturalists. However, a lot can be learnt about a wood if you record the availability of habitat of high value to insects. Together with woodland edge, some of the more important habitats are listed earlier; the likelihood that the site has a high potential for insects increases with the number of features present.

Butterflies may be surveyed in promising open areas and along shrubby woodland edges. If you are not familiar with butterfly identification, refer to field guides such as the *Pocket Guide to the Butterflies of Great Britain and Ireland* (Lewington, 2015). When you are making changes in your woodland with a view to attracting insects, such as widening a ride, you may want to measure the effect of the changes, by doing a survey beforehand and over several years after the work. The most straightforward method is to plan a transect or route through the most promising habitat, and walk this on four, evenly-spaced occasions during the flight season noting species and numbers; typically early to mid May; the first two weeks of June; mid to late July; and mid August. If any habitat specialists are known to be present, then visits should be more frequent during their flight season.

Surveys are usually carried out between 11.00 and 16.00 hrs in suitable weather conditions for butterfly activity: dry and sunny (at least 60% sunshine); no more than a moderate breeze; at least 13°C in sunny conditions or 17°C if overcast. Strictly, only butterflies occurring within a 5 m wide line transect are recorded, up to 5 m ahead of the recorder. This will allow data to be compared with other years if so desired. More details can be found on the United Kingdom Butterfly Monitoring Scheme (UKBMS) website (www.ukbms.org). Monitoring that is to be repeated year-on-year will benefit from more frequent visits; every two weeks, ideally from the beginning of April to the end of September, but particularly during the period of peak activity from late June to mid August. Volunteers may be willing to help with surveys, particularly if habitat specialist butterflies are present. For more information, contact the UKBMS or your local county Wildlife Trust.

2.3 Woodland birds

Woodland is a more complex habitat in terms of its structure and the communities which it supports than any other terrestrial habitat in Britain. Consequently, woodland, scrub and young conifer plantations support more breeding birds (some 64 species) than any other habitat. These bird communities include some species which are widespread and abundant, such as robin, great tit and chaffinch; others such as great spotted woodpecker and treecreeper are widespread but present in limited numbers; whilst species such as lesser spotted woodpecker and hawfinch are confined to relatively few woods. The numbers of woodland birds are influenced by a range of factors, of which the weather and availability of food in the winter are particularly important. Prolonged periods of severe winter weather with lying snow can have significant effects on the populations of smaller birds such as wren and goldcrest. In the breeding season, the availability of food (particularly insects) and nest sites also influences the diversity and abundance of woodland birds, although our understanding of the factors which control woodland bird populations is surprisingly limited.

Birds and woodland types
The number and diversity of birds differs between woodland types, even when these are located in close proximity. Perhaps the greatest contrast is between old-growth deciduous woodland in the lowlands, where an abundance of birds would be in stark contrast to the handful of species residing in a nearby mature spruce plantation. Every individual ancient wood is distinct in terms of its structure and floristic diversity and so woodland bird communities also differ between woods (in both species diversity and numbers), adding to this sense of uniqueness. Factors responsible for this include location, area, physical structure and the diversity of trees and shrubs. Although there is no such thing as a 'typical woodland bird community', one can identify birds which are characteristic of different woodland types.

Lowland deciduous woodlands support the richest diversity of birds, influenced to some extent by soil type, fertility and whether the woods are managed as high forest or coppice. Characteristic birds of oak and ash woods for example include wren, robin, warblers and chaffinch, which usually nest in the understorey; and hole nesters such as stock dove, woodpeckers, flycatchers, tits, nuthatch, treecreeper, jackdaw and starling.

In contrast, mature upland broadleaved woods tend to have a relatively simple structure, with a closed canopy and sparse understorey, which is often the result of heavy browsing pressure by deer and domestic stock. Chaffinch and willow warbler are the most abundant species in the upland birch woods of Scotland, along with species such as wren, robin, common redstart, wood warbler, spotted flycatcher, blue tit, great tit and coal tit. The more widely distributed upland oak woods of north and western Britain generally support fewer species and smaller populations of birds than their lowland counterparts. They may be characterised by different summer visitors, namely common redstart, pied flycatcher and wood warbler, and higher numbers of tree pipits. Resident breeding birds are similar to those found in lowland oak woods.

Native pinewoods in the Scottish Highlands support a distinctive woodland bird community, notable for capercaillie, crested tit and the endemic Scottish crossbill. Where birch and other deciduous species occur; black grouse, spotted flycatcher, willow warbler, lesser redpoll, common crossbill and siskin may also be found. In some areas, chaffinch and goldcrest are the commonest species.

It is difficult to generalise in the case of exotic conifer plantations, as the bird communities are affected by tree species and climate, and change considerably with each growth stage between planting and harvest. Communities are at their most diverse during the establishment and pre-thicket stages, when ground-nesting species such as nightjar, tree pipit, whinchat and species typical of scrub, such as dunnock and warblers may be found. Raptors such as goshawk, sparrowhawk and long-eared owls also hunt over young plantations. As trees close canopy and develop to maturity, scrub species are lost, to be replaced by those which tend to feed in the high canopy: coal tit, chaffinch and goldcrest are often the dominant species, sometimes accompanied by siskin and common crossbill.

Birds of conservation concern

Woodland management should be sympathetic to bird populations in general, but in some cases you may wish to target management to support species which are of the greatest conservation concern, as their populations are the most threatened. *The State of the UK's Birds* (e.g. Hayhow *et al.*, 2015) is a series of annual reports produced by the Royal Society for the Protection of Birds (RSPB), British Trust for Ornithology (BTO) and the Wildfowl and Wetlands Trust with the UK Government's statutory conservation agencies, which summarise the fortunes of Britain's bird populations (available online). The reports include wild-bird indicators, an update on common breeding birds and trends of scarce and rare breeding birds.

Birds of Conservation Concern 4 (also available online) is a non-statutory classification of species in decline (Eaton *et al.*, 2015). Birds of the highest concern are included on a Red List, with birds of moderate concern placed on an Amber list. Most Red-listed woodland birds and some Amber-listed species are also included on country-level Priority Species lists of birds. These reports document the plight of some woodland species which have declined dramatically, such as woodcock, lesser spotted woodpecker, pied flycatcher, spotted flycatcher, wood warbler, willow tit and hawfinch. All of these are mature woodland specialists, with specific habitat requirements, which make them particularly vulnerable to any change in the condition of a wood. The causes are not well understood, but changes in management leading to more high forest, with a loss of structural diversity, may be a contributory factor. Some generalists such as the starling, and birds of more open woodland and scrub such as tree pipit and grasshopper warbler have also declined rapidly in recent years. Nightingales are traditionally associated with coppice woodland and young plantations, but in recent decades scrub has become an increasingly important habitat (Hayhow *et al.*, 2015). Numbers of this species have declined considerably in recent years, and range contractions have also been recorded. If you are lucky enough to have nightingales in your woodland, or want to provide suitable habitat for them, consult the BTO's guide for land managers and conservation practitioners (BTO, 2015).

Survey methods

Woodland birds are relatively easy to monitor, and many woodland owners will have the skills to identify birds based on their appearance and song. If you are not familiar with bird identification, refer to a field guide such as *Collins Bird Guide* (Svensson *et al.*, 2010). You may also find the bird identifier on the RSPB website helpful, as it includes sound clips of woodland bird song. Surveys loosely based on the BTO's Breeding Bird Survey can provide you with a better understanding of the birds which visit and breed in your wood. Just two formal visits are required: the first should be made between early April and mid-May, when resident birds are breeding; the second between mid-May and late June, when migrant birds

An early morning bird walk can be a very rewarding experience.

breed (at least four weeks after the first visit). Visits may be later further north in the country. It is important to start these surveys early in the morning, when bird activity is at its height, although avoiding the period immediately after dawn when the intensity of the dawn chorus makes recording more difficult. A predetermined route through the woodland should be followed, recording all birds within 25 m, and those between 25–100 m, either side of the path. Detailed instructions and field recording sheets can be obtained from the BTO website (www.bto.org/volunteer-surveys/bbs).

When surveying, or undertaking any work in your woodland, you need to be familiar with UK legislation which protects all wild birds, their nests and eggs by law, with limited exceptions. Some rare species are given special protection; for example it is a criminal offence to disturb, at or near the nest, a species on Schedule 1 of the Act, such as hobby or goshawk. In Scotland it is also an offence to disturb capercaillie and ruff at their leks. Nesting is considered to have started as soon as nest building starts. For more detailed information it is advisable to consult the Act itself.

2.4 Woodland mammals

Terrestrial mammals

Mammals began to return to Britain after the last ice age, but flooding of the landbridge with Europe brought this to an end (Yalden, 1999). In the 'wildwood', our three largest forest carnivores, wolf, lynx and brown bear hunted herbivores such as aurochs, wild boar and beaver. Smaller carnivores included wildcat, red fox, badger, polecat and pine marten (Table 2.5). Lynx and brown bear survived in Britain at least until Roman times, whilst the wolf finally became extinct in the Middle Ages. Of their prey, red deer and roe deer survive to the present day, despite intense hunting pressure in the Middle Ages. Other large herbivores did not fare so well; auroch and elk were both extinct by the end of the Bronze Age. Wild boar finally disappeared in the Middle Ages, although they are now recolonising British woodland after escaping from domestic farms in southern England. Beavers also became extinct in the early Middle Ages, and are now the subject of several trial reintroduction programmes. Our woodland mammal fauna has also been increased by the introduction of grey squirrel and several exotic deer, including fallow deer, muntjac and Sika (Table 2.5), all of which can cause major problems in native woodland.

Deer reside mostly in woodland, but may also be found in more open farmland. Many people find them attractive, although they can be very elusive. However, when deer populations increase, they can have a major impact on woodland flora and fauna, through browsing herbs, shrubs and young trees. This can cause long-term changes to the composition of native woodland. Grey squirrels are also attractive animals, much easier to observe than deer. They were introduced from North America just over 100 years ago, and are now found in native woodland throughout Britain. Grey squirrels nest in trees and feed on a variety of nuts, fruits and shoots. They also damage trees, mainly through bark stripping on young stems (typically 10–25 cm in diameter) and branches of some mature trees. Oaks, beech and sycamore can be particularly hard hit, so that the composition of the tree community can be completely altered. Grey squirrels, which are legally classified as vermin because of the damage they do, also carry squirrelpox virus; grey squirrels have developed immunity but the disease is usually fatal for red squirrels.

Today, a number of native woodland mammals give real cause for concern, resulting in their designation as country-level Priority Species. Wildcats, pine martens and polecats were once widespread in Britain, but declined significantly due to persecution and habitat loss. The wildcat is critically endangered and is restricted to the north of Scotland. Pine martens are locally common in parts of Scotland, but very rare in England and Wales; whilst polecats, trapped to near extinction by the early 20th century, are now increasing and spreading across England from their stronghold in Wales. Habitat quality and promoting tolerance and understanding are two factors key to the polecat's continued expansion. Red squirrels live in all woodland types, but seem to prefer conifers. It is thought that their well-publicised decline is due to competition and disease transmission from grey squirrels, as has been demonstrated on Anglesey, where eradication of greys has allowed red squirrel

Pine martens are locally common in parts of Scotland, but very rare in England and Wales.

numbers to increase. Conservation measures include the use of feeders which provide food for red squirrels but not greys, and attempts to keep greys from colonising red squirrel strongholds, such as Scotland's native pinewoods.

The dormouse is a European Protected Species which has declined in Britain over the last century, with the loss of ancient woodland, fragmentation and the decline in coppicing likely to be key factors. It is a nocturnal animal, which spends most of its time off the ground when active, feeding on a variety of food including flowers, berries, nuts and insects. Nests may be woven in shrubs, but the dormouse prefers old bird nests, squirrel dreys or hollow tree branches. The best way to find out if this exceptionally secretive animal lives in your wood is to search for signs, such as nests of shredded honeysuckle bark woven into a ball, or the characteristic neat hole gnawed in an opened hazel nut. Dormice can be encouraged in woodland by putting up nestboxes (see Section 5.3).

Grey squirrels are the most easily observed mammal in British woodlands, but many terrestrial mammals like the dormouse are secretive or nocturnal, and difficult to see, especially in woodland. Badgers are also largely nocturnal, so setts, trails and signs are more likely to be encountered than the animals themselves. Badger setts are usually located close to the edge of woodland, in areas where the soil is easily dug and well drained. The most obvious feature of a sett is the large mound of earth, containing excavated soil and stones. A 'funnel' shaped entrance usually leads down into the ground at an angle of 45°. If you are fortunate to have an active sett in your wood, you may wish to observe the animals. Contact your local badger group, who will be able to offer expert advice on how to successfully observe these shy and retiring animals, and may visit with you.

Red foxes in contrast may be encountered along the woodland edge, sometimes basking in the early morning sunshine with their cubs. Red squirrels can be seen where their numbers are high, especially around artificial feeding stations. Native red and roe deer are easier to observe along the woodland edge or in open areas. You would have to be very lucky to see a polecat or pine marten – the closely related stoat and weasel are much more likely to be encountered, scurrying along woodland rides. Perhaps the most secretive mammal of all is the extremely rare wildcat, a solitary animal which hunts predominantly at night.

Bats

Bats are also very difficult to observe in woodland, even for experts using bat detectors. Consequently far less is known about how bats use woodland compared with other habitats such as meadows and open water, or roosts in old buildings. However, we do know that all 17 species of British bats regularly use woodlands and that some are woodland

Table 2.5
Mammals found in woodland habitats in Britain.

Native		Introduced
Hedgehog*	Harvest mouse*	Brown hare*
Common shrew	Red fox	European rabbit
Pygmy shrew	Weasel	Grey squirrel
Water shrew	Stoat	Wild boar (re-colonising)
Mole	Polecat*	Fallow deer
Red squirrel*	Pine marten*	Sika deer
Dormouse*	Badger	Muntjac deer
Bank vole	Wildcat*	Chinese water deer
Field vole	Red deer	
Wood mouse	Roe deer	
Yellow-necked mouse		

* Country-level Priority Species;

specialists (Table 2.6). The abundance of insects in older woods provides a variety of feeding opportunities, whilst old trees with their numerous cracks, crevices, and woodpecker holes, and ivy-clad trees support roosts and maternity colonies.

Studies using lures to capture bats in woodlands in South East England have recently established a clear association between structurally diverse mature woodland with a well-developed understorey and the number and diversity of bat species (Hill and Greenaway, 2008). The implications of this study are clear – that reinstatement of management in a wood which has a dense understorey should only be undertaken after a thorough bat survey has been carried out.

The ideal landscape for bats would include a mosaic of different habitats for feeding, roosting and commuting; including ancient woodland, riparian woodland, scrub, hedgerows, semi-natural grassland and some open water. One hundred years ago, such a landscape may have been common in the countryside, providing insect food in abundance, but not so today.

Table 2.6
The status and use of woodland by Britain's bats. Sources: Altringham (2003); Bat Conservation Trust; Battersby and TMP (2005); Harris *et al*. 1995; Vincent Wildlife Trust.

Species	Status and distribution	Use of woodland
Greater horseshoe bat*	S. Wales, South West, very rare and endangered	Forages over deciduous woodland, diet predominately beetles and moths
Lesser horseshoe bat*	S. Wales, borders (as far west as Oxfordshire), South West, rare and endangered	Forages in deciduous woodland, diet of flies and small moths
Bechstein's bat*	Very rare	Forages in mature woodland with diverse structure
Natterer's bat	Widespread, relatively scarce	Forages in variety of woodland habitats, diet includes wide range of insects and spiders
Daubenton's bat	Widespread, population estimates poor	Forages along riparian woodland and other woodland, diet of insects and aquatic larvae
Whiskered bat	Widespread but local	Hawks over woodland, edge and rides, diet of moths, spiders and wide range of insects
Brandt's bat	Common in N. and W. England	Similar habits and diet to whiskered bat
Alcathoe bat*	Recently discovered in Yorkshire, Sussex and West Midlands	Foraging habitat and diet unknown, probably similar to whiskered bat; considered to be a woodland specialist
Serotine	Declining in South East England, population estimates poor	Forages along woodland edge, diet of beetles, moths and other insects
Noctule*	England and Wales, uncommon	Forages along woodland edge/glades, diet of beetles, flies and moths
Leisler's bat*	England, scarce	Forages along woodland edge/glades, and over canopy, diet of flies and other small insects
Common pipistrelle	Widespread, population estimates poor	Forages along woodland edge and rides, diet of flies and other insects
Soprano pipistrelle	Widespread, population estimates poor	Forages along woodland edge and rides, diet of flies and other insects
Nathusius' pipistrelle	Rare	Lowland woods, diet includes flies
Brown long-eared bat	Widespread	Gleans from foliage/other surfaces in woodland and edge, diet includes wide range of insects and spiders
Grey long-eared bat	Southern England, very rare	Gleans from foliage/other surfaces in woodland and edge, diet includes moths
Barbastelle*	Widespread, very rare	Forages in woodland canopy and edge, diet includes moths

* woodland specialist

Agricultural intensification and development has led to the loss or degradation of feeding habitat and to the destruction of natural and artificial roost sites, such as ivy clad trees and barns. As a result, most British bat species have declined over the past century, and some have suffered range contractions. Although the National Bat Monitoring Programme (NBMP) showed an 18% increase in bat populations between 1999 and 2012, this has to be viewed in the context of historical severe declines in bat populations (Bat Conservation Trust, 2014). All species are listed on the EU Habitats Directive Annex IV, with Bechstein's, barbastelle, lesser horseshoe and greater horseshoe bats – all woodland specialists – being given extra protection on Annex II. These, together with noctule (also a woodland specialist), soprano pipistrelle and brown long-eared bat are also country-level Priority Species, whilst Bechstein's bat and the barbastelle are on the IUCN Red List of Near Threatened Species.

Survey methods

General sightings and signs of mammals can be recorded during any visit to your woodland, noting down observations of animals and signs such as tracks or droppings. The BTO's Breeding Bird Survey guidelines include useful information on mammal recording. Active badger setts, squirrel dreys and fox dens may also be recorded. Anecdotal evidence from neighbouring woodland owners may also be important, especially for elusive creatures such as dormouse and pine marten. It should be assumed that dormice are present in any wood within their range, especially in southern England, unless proven otherwise. One of the easiest ways of establishing the presence of dormice is to examine gnawed hazelnuts in the autumn. The illustration below shows hazelnuts gnawed by different small mammals, but only the dormouse leaves a smooth round opening, distinguishing it from mice, voles and squirrels. The best time to look for nuts is from mid-August through to the end of the year, when the nuts are relatively fresh. Older nuts gradually decay, making it more difficult to discern the teeth marks of other small rodents. If hazel is absent from your wood, look in nearby hedgerows and woodlands, on the assumption that if dormice are present close by, there is every chance that they will be present in your wood. Further information can be found in *The Dormouse Conservation Handbook* (Bright *et al.*, 2006).

Specialist surveys are most appropriate when the presence of species of conservation concern is suspected, especially if management activities are planned which might cause

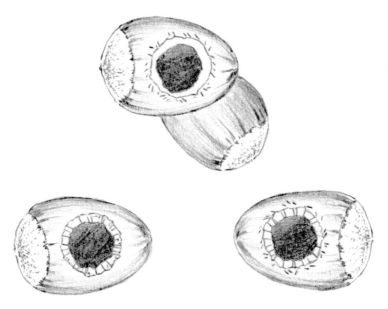

Close examination of a hazelnut will tell you which animal has been gnawing it; the dormouse (top) carves a smooth inner rim, with teeth marks on the surface of the nut at an angle to the hole; the wood mouse (lower right) leaves parallel toothmarks on the inner rim, and teeth marks on the surface; bank voles (lower left) leave parallel grooves on the inner rim, with no marks on the nut surface.

disturbance. Dormice surveys for example might require the use of nest tubes or nest boxes, especially if hazel is not present in the wood. For specialist surveys such as these, advice must be sought from the statutory conservation agency prior to asking an experienced ecologist with a dormouse licence to undertake a survey appropriate to the species concerned (for a summary of methods, see Institute of Environmental Assessment, 1995; Bright *et al.*, 2006).

Some bat species such as pipistrelles may be observed at dusk, feeding along woodland margins and rides, others such Daubenton's bat may be seen foraging along a woodland stream. But most species require bat detectors, which can be purchased from ecological suppliers. These pick up bat calls using an ultrasonic microphone, which can be tuned to different frequencies to detect different species, although some training in their use is advised. However, bats are very difficult to survey in woodland, even for experts with sophisticated bat detectors. Volunteers from local bat groups may be interested to survey your woodland, particularly if the habitat looks promising for bats. A relatively simple visual assessment of your wood should provide a good indication of the likelihood that bats are feeding and roosting there. The age and condition of the trees is the most important factor, as most tree species can support bats. If the wood contains any trees with holes or crevices offering protection, then bats could be present. Older trees, particularly if they have been damaged have a good chance of supporting roosting bats, and the chances are very much increased for veteran trees, with their diversity of rot holes, crevices, splits, snags and loose bark (see Section 4.4). In fact any deadwood attached to standing trees could support bats. Older trees covered by dense ivy or other dense climbers may also support roosting bats, and should be protected for this reason. The size of the wood is also important, with respect to the actual species which might be present. Some woodland specialists such as Bechstein's bat require woods of at least 25 ha, whereas other species such as noctule and long-eared bat may roost in very small woods. In particularly favourable habitat, bat experts with acoustic lures might be persuaded to visit the wood, especially if there is a chance of finding rare and threatened species such as Bechstein's bat or the barbastelle. The Bat Conservation Trust should be able to provide contact details for local bat groups; the Trust is also interested in recruiting volunteers to help with the NBMP (www.bats.org.uk/pages/nbmp.htm).

Surveys assume much greater importance if management work is planned at any time of the year, as they can lower the risk of disturbing roosting bats as well as enabling woods to be managed to promote their value for bats. Roost surveys should be carried out in both winter and summer, so they need to be planned well in advance of any management operations. If carrying out a winter survey, it is important to systematically examine trees in discrete blocks, to avoid missing any roost trees. Inspect trees closely with binoculars, looking for potential roosting sites described above. Woods should be visited again in mid-summer, preferably just before sunset on very warm days, when the high-pitched squeaks of bats may be heard (by younger people) as bats become active. Further details may be found in the Forestry Commission's *Woodland management for bats* (Forestry Commission, 2005) and Bat Conservation Trust's *Bat Surveys* (Hundt, 2012) which are freely available on the internet.

2.5 Amphibians and reptiles

Britain has far fewer amphibians and reptiles in comparison to mainland Europe, with only 13 native terrestrial amphibians and reptiles, all of which are protected to varying degrees (Table 2.7). The pool frog, which is now believed to be a native species in Britain, became extinct here in 1995, but has since been reintroduced. With the exception of pool frog and natterjack toad, all British amphibians can occur in suitable ponds and wetland habitat in woodland. Of these, the common toad is a country-level Priority Species and the great crested newt is a European Protected Species and a country-level Priority Species, in recognition of major declines in their populations resulting from habitat loss and degradation. All amphibians require water bodies for breeding, although the amount of time they spend in water and their specific requirements differs between species. They also spend a considerable part of their lives on land, so the terrestrial habitat surrounding water bodies is of considerable importance. In general, the landscape within a kilometre or so of breeding ponds is likely to comprise a mix of semi-natural pasture, with scrub, hedgerows and woodland. Structural diversity in semi-natural grassland is important for shelter, and for invertebrates for foraging amphibians.

British reptiles occur in a wide range of habitats, including lowland heath, moorland, tussocky grassland and woodland. Adder, grass snake, slow-worm and viviparous lizard are widespread, and may be found in woodland rides and glades, bramble thickets, log piles and clear-felled forest. Sand lizard and smooth snake are very localised in southern England, often on the same sites, although sand lizard also occurs in Merseyside sand dunes. These rare reptiles are more usually associated with heathland and other open habitat, but both will use woodland edge, rides, clear felled or young restock sites and open pine stands. Any mechanised operations such as felling, spraying and mowing could harm these reptiles as they cannot move quickly enough to escape the threat.

If reptiles or amphibians might be present in a wood where management operations are being planned, surveys based on current best practice should be undertaken, with a view to implementing a mitigation programme if necessary. For further information, the *Herpetofauna Workers Manual* (Gent and Gibson, 2012) provides comprehensive guidance to all aspects of reptile and amphibian conservation and management, including site assessment, species translocation and the law. Natural England's *Reptiles: guidelines for developers* (English Nature, 2004) and Amphibian and Reptile Conservation's *Reptile Habitat Management Handbook* (Edgar *et al.*, 2010) should also be consulted, together with the latest environmental management guidance on the GOV.UK website. Guidance specifically for great crested newts is also available (e.g. Forestry Commission and Natural England, 2013; Forestry Commission Scotland and Scottish Natural Heritage, 2009; Langton *et al.*, 2001).

If European Protected Species are present, a very careful and well planned approach to woodland management is required. Specialist advice may be needed to help identify areas where animals rest, breed and hibernate. Guidance notes on managing woodlands for individual European Protected Species are available on the Forestry Commission and Natural England websites.

Table 2.7
Britain's terrestrial amphibians and reptiles and their conservation status.

	Country-level Priority Species	European Protected Species
Amphibians		
Common frog		
Common toad	*	
Great crested newt	*	*
Natterjack toad	*	*
Palmate newt		
Pool frog	*	
Smooth newt		
Reptiles		
Adder	*	
Grass snake	*	
Sand lizard	*	*
Slow worm	*	
Smooth snake	*	*
Viviparous lizard	*	

Surveys

The Field Studies Council's *Guide to the Reptiles and Amphibians of Britain and Ireland* (Roberts and Ovenden, 2003) should prove useful if you undertake surveys of reptiles in your own wood. Reptile activity is highly seasonal; animals hibernate between October and March, and their activity during the summer months is dependent on the weather. Reptiles may even go into partial hibernation in prolonged periods of hot weather (aestivation). Consequently reptile surveys should be considered well in advance of any forestry operations. Reptile surveyors usually search for animals which are basking or lying under warm objects, and use artificial refugia as part of a survey. These are usually sheets of corrugated metal, roofing felt or a similar material, typically 70 x 70 cm, placed in sunny locations away from public routeways. If adders are likely to be present, stout boots should be worn and a stick or adder proof glove used to lift the artificial refugia, as an adder bite can cause poisoning or an allergic reaction. The best time to look for reptiles is in the spring, when animals tend to bask for longer in the cooler temperatures. In April, the best time of day is 11 am–3 pm; in late spring, mid morning and late afternoon are better. You could also carry out surveys in the autumn, whilst summer tends to be much more variable and difficult in very warm weather. Walk slowly, scanning from side to side and ahead in sunny areas, looking particularly at sheltered spots, and short vegetation where it occurs close to denser cover.

Surveys of amphibians on sites that support great crested newt can only be undertaken by surveyors with the necessary expertise and licence. Breeding ponds may be surveyed on several occasions using different techniques, including a visual search for eggs and bottle trapping. Night time searches by torchlight can be undertaken, but only with a licence as this is likely to disturb great crested newts. You may undertake casual searches in spring for the long gelatinous strings of toad spawn or clumps frogspawn in a pond, but eggs of newts

Surveying artificial refugia for reptiles in a woodland glade. Note a stick was used to lift the sheet initially.

are attached to leaves of variety of plants, and can be difficult to find. Tadpoles may also be observed; frog tadpoles are initially dark, becoming mottled with bronze spots, whilst toad tadpoles remain very dark.

Guides to amphibian and reptile identification may be found in the appropriate Survey Pack, freely available on the National Amphibian and Reptile Recording Scheme (NARRS) website.

2.6 **Woodland fungi**

Woodland supports the richest diversity of fungi of any habitat in Britain, where they fulfil the essential role of recycling nutrients. It is the fruiting body – the mushroom or toadstool – which is most familiar, but fungi also possess thread-like hyphae, which form a web of mycelium, often out of sight, for example in the soil, litter or roots of trees.

Woodland fungi are mainly associated with the decomposition of leaf litter and wood, whilst a group called 'mycorrhizal' fungi (literally 'fungus root') form mutually beneficial 'symbiotic' relationships with plants. Others such as the rusts and smuts are parasites of woodland plants, and lichen-forming fungi are essentially partners with their algal partners (see Section 2.7).

Mycorrhizal fungi help plants by forming extensive networks of fine fungal hyphae which radiate out into the surrounding soil, allowing the fungi to transfer nutrients to the tree from a much greater volume of soil than the tree's own root system. The relationship is symbiotic because the fungi gain sugars from the plant. There are two main types of 'mycorrhizae' which associate with trees, known as ectomycorrhizae and arbuscular mycorrhizae. Ectomycorrhizae form a sheath of fungal threads around the outside of tree roots which extends between the plant's cells, but does not penetrate them. Trees typical of more impoverished soils (which include the majority of British trees) tend to have ectomycorrhizal fungi; good examples are fly agaric on birch and amethyst deceiver on beech. Arbuscular mycorrhizae live within the roots and actually penetrate cells of the plant. They may be found on ash and field maple, although many produce no fruiting bodies, and are therefore difficult to observe.

The richest assemblages of fungi tend to be found in ancient woodland which has been unmanaged for a long period of time (Table 2.8). Here, many species prefer the damp

Table 2.8
Factors affecting fungal diversity in woodland (after Spooner and Roberts, 2005).

Factor	Fungal community
Woodland composition	Dependent on the woodland type, for example different mix of species in lowland oak wood compared to native pinewood; species richness increased by greater diversity of trees and shrubs
Soil composition	Affected by soil pH and presence or absence of litter
Climate and location	Some species restricted to regions of Britain; shelter can also influence diversity
Moisture	Strongly affected by ground moisture levels, humidity and rainfall (some species favour the west or east of Britain as a result)
Management	Historical management and current practices are important – very different communities may be found in unmanaged ancient woodland with abundant deadwood compared to heavily grazed woodland or an actively coppiced wood with low tree species diversity
Age	Ancient woodland tends to support more species than more recent woods or plantations; some lichens may offer clues to the age of a wood, but no macrofungi equivalent of ancient woodland indicator plants
Size	Larger woods usually contain more diverse habitat niches, and tend therefore to be richer for fungi

and shady conditions of the high forest. Wood pasture containing veteran trees – often pollarded – is also a rich hunting ground for fungi, especially rare species. Surprisingly, conifer plantations can also contain rich assemblages of species, particularly those planted with Scots pine, although many of the species associated with native pinewoods in Scotland are absent south of the border. A provisional Red List for Threatened British Fungi including nearly 400 species (Evans *et al.*, 2006) was followed by publication of the Red List for Boletaceae (Ainsworth *et al.*, 2013). Many of the species listed in the provisional Red List are found in woodland. Threats to these fungi include the clearing up of fallen 'deadwood' and commercial collecting.

Fungal forays

Fungal forays have increased in popularity in recent years, and provide a good opportunity for you to gain some appreciation of the fungal community present in your own wood. A useful beginner's guide is *Fungi (RSPB Pocket Nature)* (Evans and Kibby, 2004) or the more comprehensive *Collins Complete British Mushrooms and Toadstools* (Sterry and Hughes, 2009). The following tables list some of the commoner species which might be encountered in mixed deciduous woodland, which collectively represent a range of shapes, colours and sizes:

Fungi which associate with plant roots

Deathcap	*Amanita phalloides*	Mild milkcap	*L. subdulcis*
Red cracking bolete	*Boletus chrysenteron*	Brown birch bolete	*Leccinum scabrum*
Penny bun	*B. edulis*	Brown rollrim	*Paxillus involutus*
Scarletina bolete	*B. luridiformis*	Purple brittlegill	*Russula atropurpurea*
Chanterelle	*Cantharellus cibarius*	Ochre brittlegill	*R. ochroleuca*
Purple stocking webcap	*Cortinarius mucifluoides*	Common earthball	*Scleroderma citrinum*
Poisonpie	*Hebeloma crustuliniforme*	Earthfan	*Thelephora terrestris*
Oakbug milkcap	*Lactarius quietus*	Blue spot knight	*Tricholoma columbetta*

Fungi which associate with wood

Jelly ear	*Auricularia auricula-judae*	Coral spot	*Nectria cinnabarina*
Smoky bracket	*Bjerkandera adusta*	Wrinkled crust	*Phlebia radiata*
Glistening inkcap	*Coprinellus micaceus*	Shaggy scalycap	*Pholiota squarrosa*
Oak mazegill	*Daedalea quercina*	Birch polypore	*Piptoporus betulinus*
Blushing bracket	*Daedaleopsis confragosa*	Scarlet elf cup	*Sarcoscypha austriaca*
King Alfred's cakes	*Daldinia concentrica*	Hairy curtain crust	*Stereum hirsutum*
Southern bracket	*Ganoderma australe*	Lumpy bracket	*Trametes gibbosa*
Sulphur tuft	*Hypholoma fasciculare*	Turkeytail	*T. versicolor*
Beech woodwart	*Hypoxylon fragiforme*	Yellow brain fungus	*Tremella mesenterica*
Stump puffball	*Lycoperdon pyriforme*	Waxy crust	*Vuilleminia comedens*
Common bonnet	*Mycena galericulata*	Candlesnuff fungus	*Xylaria hypoxylon*

Litter-inhabiting fungi

Clouded funnel	*Clitocybe nebularis*	Leaf parachute	*Marasmius epiphyllus*
Russet toughshank	*Gymnopus dryophilus*	Collared parachute	*M. rotula*
Wood woollyfoot	*G. peronatus*	Dog stinkhorn	*Mutinus caninus*
Tawny funnel	*Lepista flaccida*	Milking bonnet	*Mycena galopus*
Slender club	*Macrotyphula juncea*	Lilac bonnet	*M. pura*

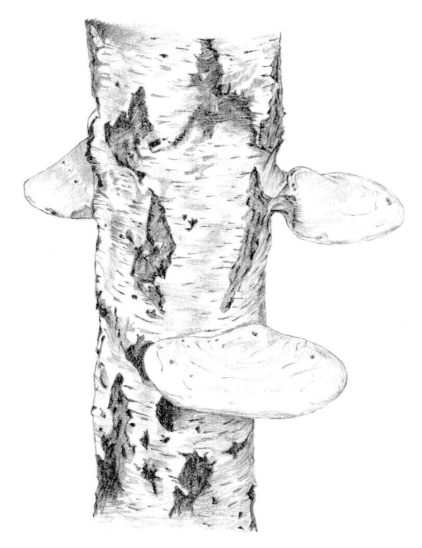

Birch polypore (*Piptoporus betulinus*) on a dead standing birch tree.

Eating wild fungi has become popular in recent years, so there may be a temptation to collect fungi found on a fungal foray. It is important to remember that many fungi are poisonous, and can result in severe illness or even death. Consequently, a good field guide should be used, and collecting fungi to eat is entirely at the reader's own risk.

2.7 Lichens

Lichens as a group are very colourful, and are surely familiar to most people, as they occur in urban as well as rural environments. They have an intrinsic beauty which inspires many people to photograph them, even if their true identify might remain a mystery. Lichens are not a single organism like a plant, but two separate life-forms, a fungus and an alga or cyanobacterium, which live together in a stable, self-supporting or 'symbiotic' relationship. Thus, 'lichen' is a biological term which essentially describes a fungal lifestyle, rather than a taxonomic group.

What you see with the naked eye is known as the 'thallus', which is the body of the lichen, whose form is determined by the fungus. This is made up of several levels; the surface or cortex comprises densely packed fungal hyphae, below which the alga is to be found. Unlike many plants, lichens can be observed and potentially identified at any time of the year. Macrolichens are the most conspicuous and the easiest group to identify. Fruticose lichens may be shrubby, beard-like or hair-like in appearance. Foliose lichens are more leaf-like, with upper and lower surfaces which are distinctly different. The majority of lichens in Britain however are variations on the crustose form, which are closely attached to the substrate, which is often the bark of trees. Many such lichens require specialist knowledge and the use of a microscope or chemical tests to identify. However, the Field Studies Council has several fold-out charts for beginners (www.fieldstudiescouncil.org.uk).

Lichens are also now used as Indices of Ecological Continuity for various woodland types, following the pioneering work of Francis Rose. 'Ancient woodland indicator' lichens are far more sensitive than plants, because rare lichens associated with old trees once lost, may take centuries to return. The number of indicator species in a wood is used to indicate the continuity of the woodland canopy, and can identify woodland which dates back to the early medieval period, or earlier.

For lichens, structural diversity in woodland is almost as important as its historical continuity. Most lichens require some light, so woods with open areas, and trees of different ages, usually host a greater diversity of lichen species. Veteran trees, often to be found in ancient wood pasture contain many specialist habitat niches for woodland lichens, which also have poor colonisation abilities. These ancient habitats are a magnet for lichenologists. Managed woods with even-aged canopies or coppice on the other hand generally support far fewer species, even if the woods are ancient in origin. Lichens are also sensitive to atmospheric pollutants such as sulphur dioxide, which is a further influence on their distribution.

The other main factors determining lichen distribution are climate and woodland type. In the west of Scotland for example, rich and luxuriant assemblages of macrolichens can be found in the wet, mossy oak-hazel woods on lower ground. Upland oak woods at higher elevations also have a western, Atlantic distribution, and support rich lichen communities, though lacking some of the specialities of the coastal woods. These oak woods are also rich in mosses, liverworts and ferns. The Caledonian pinewoods have their own distinctive lichen flora, which in contrast to deciduous woods is mainly to be found on standing deadwood and stumps. In the more continental climate of much of lowland south eastern Britain, oceanic lichens are replaced by those with a more continental distribution.

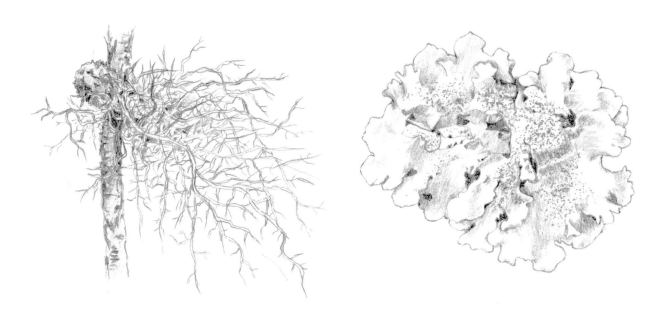

The fruticose (shrubby) lichens (left) and the foliose (flat leafy) ones (right) constitute the macrolichens.

2.8 The value of non-native trees for wildlife

A wide variety of 'exotic' trees and shrubs have been introduced into Britain, most of which are contained in arboreta, parks and gardens. Amongst these, a small number of broadleaved species have become naturalised (i.e. ecologically adapted and self-perpetuating) in our native woods, including sweet chestnut, sycamore, Norway maple, red oak and horse chestnut, as well as several conifers which have spread from plantations. Small numbers of these species rarely change the character of a wood, but some have been planted extensively on ancient woodland sites. You may have some concerns about the value of these trees for wildlife.

Sweet chestnut, originally introduced from Southern Europe by the Romans, forms extensive coppice stands, often with oak standards, in many woods of South East England, having replaced more diverse tree and shrub communities. While chestnut coppice appears to have little effect on the ground flora of native woodland that it replaced, a recent review concluded that it supports many other species of fungi, invertebrates, birds and mammals associated with native broadleaved woods on similar site types, although the number and variety tended to be lower, especially in monoculture stands (Buckley and Howell, 2004). For example, Kennedy and Southwood (1984) listed just 11 species of insects occurring on chestnut, in comparison to over 400 species which use oak, and a similar number using willows. However, this is at least partly the consequence of limited survey data and the often low abundance, within the wider landscape, of the non-native tree species in question. More recent evidence suggests that sweet chestnut is an important and perhaps undervalued host plant for moths, with the larval stages of up to 72 species recorded as feeding on it (Parsons and Greatorex-Davies, 2006) including nationally scarce species such as scarce merveille du jour and waved carpet. Maintenance of the coppice cycle in commercially viable chestnut crops can also be beneficial to some notable species that are dependent upon young growth stages which support a wide variety of woodland plants. Butterflies and moths such as the nationally scarce plume moth may benefit from the woodland herbs in young coppice. The system of relatively small coupe sizes and extensive ride networks present in worked coppice also adds diversity at the whole forest scale. Understorey woodland birds such as nightingale and willow warbler are unlikely to be numerous in chestnut coppice due to the paucity of insects. Bats may also suffer due to the lack of roost sites in mature and veteran trees.

Sycamore is a more recent introduction to Britain, probably dating back to mediaeval times. It is found mainly in England, but some woods in Scotland and Wales are dominated by sycamores. It grows on a wide range of sites, and resembles ash in its ecological requirements. Recent research suggests that ash and sycamore may be able to coexist on the same site, with alternating generations of seedlings capable of forming mixed canopies over time (Savill et al., 1997). Kennedy and Southwood (1984) listed 43 insect species on sycamore, which include a number of species of conservation concern. The base-rich bark of sycamore is also valuable for epiphytes: 170 lichens have been found on it and abundant aphid populations on its leaves provide food for woodland birds.

Plantations

Some coniferous trees have also become naturalised in Britain, including Douglas fir, European larch, European silver-fir, lodgepole pine, Scots pine (in the south of Britain, outside its native range), Western hemlock, Norway spruce and Sitka spruce. These trees have had far greater ecological effects in Britain than introduced deciduous, broadleaved trees. Many were planted on land of low agricultural value, such as sandy heaths, lowland acid soils, and upland peat bogs. When introduced into native woodland, some species might affect the diversity of woodland plants, depending on the shade they cast and how long they have been established. Plantations on moorland however have a profound effect on the ground flora, resulting in the loss of more species on each successive rotation.

Relatively little quantitative work has been carried out to compare, objectively, the biodiversity of planted and semi-natural woodlands. A five-year programme by the Forestry Commission in the UK made biodiversity assessments of plantations in the late 1990s, using a range of study sites, tree ages and species (Humphrey *et al.*, 2003). Sitka spruce, Norway spruce, Corsican pine, Scots pine and oak were examined at different growth stages: pre-thicket (8–10 years); mid-rotation (20–30 years), mature (50–80 years) and over mature (60–250 years). Native oak and semi-natural stands of Scots pine were added as 'controls'.

Assessments were taken of: vertical foliage cover, dead wood, fungi, vascular plants, bryophytes and lichens, invertebrates (present in deadwood, in the canopy, sub-canopy and on the ground) and breeding birds. More than 2,000 species were recorded, of which nearly 50% were invertebrates[1]. The lowland stands of Scots pine and Norway spruce were richest in invertebrates, and sites in northern Britain in general had less species-rich invertebrate communities, but were richer in bryophytes and lichens. The semi-natural stands examined were comparatively richer in vascular plants and lichens; but there were fewer of them than in the commercial crops. Plantations were good for hoverflies and beetles. For birds, young, pre-thicket stands made an important contribution to diversity, with such species as hen harrier, short-eared owl, woodlark and tree pipit; while there were conifer specialists such as goshawk, capercaillie, crested tit, siskin and crossbill. The conclusion is that the maturing plantations seem to have plenty of scope for biodiversity in its broadest sense and will 'improve' over time.

Returning to the ecological effects of introduced tree species in Britain, Peterken (2001) pointed out a number of instances where such species have caused long-term ecological damage. These include the vigorous spread of rhododendron into native woods on acid soils and the afforestation of moors and heaths with spruce and other conifers. However, in mitigation we would expect some long-term assimilation of less obviously damaging 'exotics' such as sweet chestnut and sycamore, which have already become colonised by native flora and fauna.

---

1 Including 202 beetles and 59 ground beetles: although this is only a fraction of the 30,000 named species of invertebrates in Britain.

3 Practical silvicultural management and wildlife

3.1 Natural versus managed forests

It almost goes without saying that the composition of your wood and the way in which it is, or has been managed, will determine its value for wildlife. There is currently great interest in converting and diversifying woods to create more 'nature-like' or 'close-to-nature' structures in the hope and expectation that they will deliver greater biodiversity benefits. We ask four questions here:

- What kind of natural forest structure would result in the absence of any management?
- To what extent are these structures emulated by different silvicultural management systems?
- Which structural types deliver the best 'value' in terms of their attractiveness to wildlife?
- What are the practical implications of a given silvicultural system for small woods?

In nature, as well as in managed forests, woods are constantly being shaped by natural processes and disturbances such as windthrow, fire, flooding, pests and diseases, and grazing by deer and other animals. These events continually create gaps in the canopy, allowing space for natural regeneration to occur and for the development, over time, of a multi-aged canopy mosaic at various scales and densities. In Britain the natural pattern of disturbance is generally small-scale, with mature trees or small groups succumbing from time to time to winter gales, old age or disease. But there is always the risk of larger-scale damage occurring infrequently at much longer intervals, as in the 1987 storm that devastated woods in South East England.

We are fortunate in Britain that our high annual rainfall militates against prolonged drought and forest fires experienced on a grand scale in the Mediterranean region or the conifer forests of Canada; and also that we have (so far) escaped major episodes of defoliation by insect pests like spruce budworms and mountain pine bark beetles in North America. But still we have had bitter experience of Dutch Elm Disease in the recent past, and there are now new threats from Ash Dieback, Red Band Needle Blight, *Phytophthora ramorum* disease of larch and Acute Oak Decline. In general, the rate of gap formation, based on observations in unmanaged temperate forests worldwide, would be expected to be of the order of 0.5–2.0% of the forest area annually, implying return intervals of 50–200 years between disturbances. The problem with small woods is that they are simply too size-limited to sustain a naturalistic disturbance regime – that is, a relatively small disturbance can wipe out a major portion of the wood, leading to an imbalance of age structures, while a major event could level an entire wood. This makes it critical to decide what your woodland does best in terms of its wildlife, and what sort of age-structure distribution to aim for.

Compared with a natural disturbance regime of 0.5–2.0% of the woodland area per annum, coppice rotations of 10–20 years turn over much faster, at rates of 5–10% per year. This creates a much younger and less complex age-structure than would be 'natural'. Growing trees on longer rotations, as in commercial broadleaved and conifer plantations, would appear at first sight to be much closer to the natural rate of turnover, e.g. 2% per year for conifers on 50 year rotations, or 1% per year for hundred-year rotations of oak or beech. But at this point the analogy breaks down, because in managed forests the fixed compartment layout implies that felling will be concentrated in large areas, at a predictable time and in predictable space. At the same time few trees will be allowed to grow on into veteran or 'old-growth' stages where timber production is the objective; and it is quite likely that replacement trees will be planted rather than naturally regenerated. In the Białowieza Forest reserve in eastern Poland, 38% of the trees are over 100 years old, many with diameters exceeding 200 cm at breast height, compared with only 18% (mostly broadleaves) of the trees recorded by the Forestry Commission in a recent National Inventory of Woodlands and Trees. Studies of natural disturbance in old-growth forests in eastern North America indicate that in practice, some dominant trees may live for 300–500 years or even longer in places that avoid disturbance, whereas areas subject to more frequent disturbance will typically result in shorter life-spans. The combination of different tree species mortalities and disturbance patterns adds complexity to the forest structure, which in turn determines the diversity of species which depend upon specific forest growth stages for their survival.

3.2 Silvicultural systems

Having pointed out some contrasts between managed and unmanaged forests, we can begin to explore to what degree different silvicultural management options can reproduce aspects of a so-called natural disturbance regime. To do this, we must first briefly consider the range of silvicultural systems and the forest structures that they create, recalling R S Troup's original (1928) definition of a silvicultural system as *the process by which forest crops are removed and replaced by new crops, resulting in woodlands of a distinctive form.* Evans and Rolls, in their book on *Getting Started in Your Own Wood* (2015) also give a useful introduction to the various types.

Perhaps the most distinctive types are wood-pasture (parkland-type) systems, where the trees are widely separated and there is enough light for grazing on a pasture beneath; and coppice, where the trees are regularly cut on short rotations, never achieving full height and re-growing after cutting from the base or from root suckers, rather than relying on natural regeneration from seed. We will return to coppice later, but first it is important to review some 'high forest' systems, where the trees are grown taller and for much longer in rotation, after which they are replaced by replanting or by natural regeneration from seed of the parent canopy. Figure 3.1 shows some contrasting profiles in even-aged and uneven-aged high forest systems.

The extreme case is 'clear cutting' (or clear-felling) that removes all trees in large clearings at the end of the rotation, usually followed by replanting, resulting in an even-aged crop. In large commercial forests this creates a coarse patchwork of compartments, often at different stages in the rotation, as the size of the felling coupes (clearings) can range from 1–5 ha in the lowlands to 20 ha or more in the uplands. But coppicing too is a form of clear cutting, although much less visually drastic as the felling units here are generally much smaller, say 0.25–0.5 ha clearances, so that more of them can be fitted into a small wood, giving a range of young age-classes. There should be no need to replant if the coppice recovers well. To fell on any larger scale in a small woodland will not only defeat the object of retaining some tree cover, but also drastically reduce the variety of niches available to wildlife.

Another approach, if you already own an even-aged conifer or broadleaved plantation, is to open the canopy gradually in smaller areas, but allowing in sufficient light to encourage natural regeneration or to carry out enrichment planting of native species. Woodlands managed in this way are essentially 'shelterwoods', relying on the presence of an overhead, if temporary canopy, to provide the seed or shelter for the young crop during its establishment phase. The young trees will develop in shadier conditions than in a clear-cutting or coppicing system, but the young saplings of several species can tolerate very shaded conditions such as yew, beech, hornbeam, field maple and sycamore. With less overhead or short-term canopy cover it is possible to grow species with intermediate light requirements, including ash, oak, lime, wild cherry, sweet chestnut, rowan and whitebeam. The two-storey system creates a greater horizontal and vertical structure.

Clear cutting

Uniform shelterwood

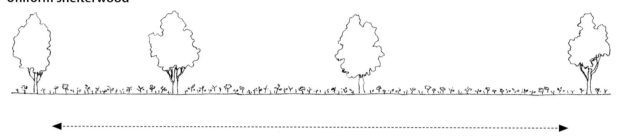

Group selection

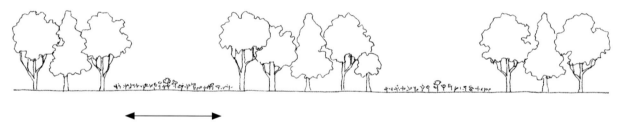

Selection

individual gap

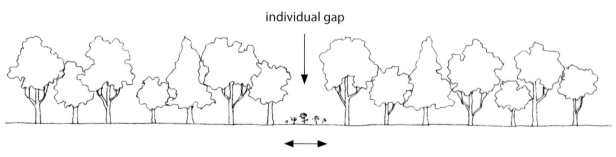

Figure 3.1 Contrasting silvicultural profiles, showing decreasing gap sizes created by harvesting from clear-cutting (top) to selection or continuous cover felling (bottom). [Felling coupe = ⟵⟶ ; the dashed line refers to a discontinuous coupe, leaving mother trees, in the case of the uniform shelterwood system].

One form of shelterwood is the 'uniform system', which requires a very rapid opening of the canopy to encourage seeding, followed by its complete removal over a short period. This creates a sudden change in the woodland environment as the two-layered vertical structure converts rapidly into a uniform monolayer after perhaps 5–10 years, when the last of the mature trees are felled. Carried out on too large a scale, uniform shelterwoods are not so dissimilar to clear cutting, and are therefore perhaps not appropriate for very small woods. There is also a very real risk of windthrow occurring during the rapid opening phase of the canopy, especially on thin or intermediately waterlogged soils. There are ways to get around this, by opening up the canopy in smaller-sized patches as strips, wedges, and groups, but they are beyond the scope of this book.

Two shelterwood types might be worth considering in small woodlands. The first is a 'group selection system', where the gaps created are much smaller than above, capable of accommodating several mature trees (say 5–10) in groups of 0.1–0.25 ha, i.e. areas of 30–50 metres or more across. Another type is an extreme shelterwood or 'selection system', in which the area of regeneration corresponds to the crown area of a mature tree that has just been felled. Within this gap the young seedlings regenerate, developing into thickets that are progressively thinned over time, until at maturity just one 'selected' tree remains standing, like its predecessor. With progressive felling over time, both systems produce intimately mixed age and size classes throughout every part of the stand, which contains seedlings, saplings, pole-stage trees, semi-mature and mature stems. Smaller gaps usually mean that only intermediate and shade-tolerant species (beech, Western hemlock, spruce and Douglas fir) can be grown, but in larger gaps (as in the group selection system) light demanders such as oak or Scots pine, as well as birches and willows, can thrive. Where the gap size is 0.25 ha or less, these shelterwoods are increasingly referred to as 'continuous cover systems'. A useful definition is:

> …. *silvicultural systems which conserve the local forest canopy/environment during the regeneration phase. Coupe size is normally below 0.25 ha (50 x 50 m) in group systems; and in shelterwood – where used – is retained for longer than 10 years. The general aim of all systems within the concept is the encouragement of diversity of structure and uneven age/size on an intimate scale* (Hart, 1995).

The system is promoted in Britain by the Continuous Cover Forestry Group (www.ccfg.org.uk) which provides useful information and technical and professional advice.

Silviculture and biodiversity

At this point we can begin to compare the relative merits of different silvicultural management systems in relation to the diversity of structure, dynamics and composition we would expect to find in natural broadleaved forests within temperate regions (Table 3.1). Desirable features are listed in the left-hand column, bearing in mind that these relate to large areas of naturally-disturbed forests. An obvious main difference is that none of the main commercial management systems allow very old (veteran) trees to develop, hence denying a significant biodiversity niche for fungi, lichens, saproxylic insects, hole-nesting birds and bats that all make use of deadwood (see Sections 4.3 and 4.4). Exceptions are the rotting wood present in pollards in wood pastures, old coppice stools and sometimes old standard trees in neglected, coppice-with-standards woods. The canopy gap size and turnover is also unnaturally faster in coppice rotations (although slower when standard trees are retained) and gaps are even bigger in clear-cut plantations. In terms of the amount of permanent open space, there is much debate about how much was present in the original forests of north west Europe, but the general consensus points to forests in Britain being relatively closed.

Management continually opens up the forest, creating a relatively high proportion of (temporary) open space in all systems, most notably in clear-cutting, coppice and wood-pasture systems. In some ways this can be regarded as an advantage over the natural state,

Table 3.1
Contrasts in structure, dynamics and composition between natural, temperate broadleaved forest and different types of managed wood. Features that are emphasised or reduced in managed woods, compared with natural woodland, are shown as positive or negative symbols; or (o) if no change. Uniform shelterwoods are omitted, but would show some affinity with clear-cutting (modified from Peterken, 1996).

Feature	Natural woodland	Shelterwoods		Clear-cutting	Coppice	Wood pasture
		Group selection	Selection			
Maximum tree age (years)	300–500	−	−	− −	− − −*	(o)
Average final tree age (years)	c.200	−	−	− −	− − −*	
Tree species diversity	mixed	−	−	− − −	(o)	− −
Gap size	mainly small	(o)	(o)	+ + +	+ +	n/a
Gap creation rate/year	1%	(o)	(o)	(o)	+ + +*	n/a
Permanent open space	little	+	+	+ +	+ +	+ + +
Structural diversity (stand level)	high	(o)	−	− − −	− −	−
Structural diversity (whole forest)	patchy	(o)	−	+ +	+ +	+ +
Dead wood	abundant	−	−	−	− − −*	−

* modified in the case of coppice-with-standards

as open-ground species such as some small mammals, birds and butterflies can also thrive in this environment.

Structural diversity – the variation in horizontal and vertical structure present either at the scale of the stand, or the whole wood – is very different in most of the managed systems from what we would expect in a natural wood. In shelterwoods, trees of different age-classes are usually present in the same compartment, giving a variation in canopy structure. However, because of the relatively large size of the felling coupe in clear-cutting and coppice systems, they are less spatially diverse *within* the felling coupes, which therefore tend to be even-aged. But at a landscape, whole-wood scale this creates big contrasts *between* adjacent areas of felling young, intermediate and older growth stages. If your wood is part of a larger woodland area, the age structure within your section, though not covering all ages, may be very different from that in neighbouring woods, making an overall patchwork of management styles and growth stages. You should consider this wider context when drawing up management plans to promote biodiversity.

You may have noticed in Table 3.1 that the silvicultural systems containing features most closely corresponding to the natural state are intimate shelterwoods, using the group selection and selection systems. These both produce a patchy and highly diverse canopy structure, usually containing more than one tree species, grown on long rotations. Furthermore, the small coupe size means that several units at different growth stages can be fitted into a small wood. However, we should be cautious before recommending them as the 'best' systems to promote biodiversity in every case. There is some evidence-based research in this area using chronosequences, often of former coppice, showing that coppicing generally increases botanical diversity, but also that old-growth promotes a wide range of fungi and insects that depend upon dead and dying wood. The situation becomes complicated as the requirements of more and more species groups are taken into consideration. It will also depend on the inherent species-richness of your wood, and on whether it contains any species of particular conservation importance that have specific

Non-intervention: the ultimate management solution?

Suppose for a moment that you decide to not to carry out any management in your woodland – what would happen? There is a good chance that parts of your ownership – even all of it – will be even-aged, whether as coppice stands or conifer or broadleaved plantations. In this case, the structure will gradually diversify over decades as subordinate trees are suppressed by their dominant neighbours – i.e. the same trees that would normally be removed in thinning operations or cut back during coppicing – creating a deadwood resource. At the same time, gaps will begin to appear in the canopy through natural disturbances – wind, disease, squirrel damage, etc., creating more deadwood. Eventually these gaps will expand in size until the point is reached where enough light filters through the ageing canopy to allow tree seedlings and a shrub layer to develop from sources dispersed from within or outside the wood. This is the beginning of an embryonic uneven-aged structure, with old trees, deadwood, young regeneration and thickets side by side, but it may take 50–100 years to reach this stage, depending on the starting point.

A means of increasing biodiversity, the *laissez-faire* option sounds attractive at first, but there are a few drawbacks to consider. All even-aged stands will pass through a long, dark phase after first canopy closure, especially if unthinned, when the light levels typically fall to 1–5% of that in the open. This will eliminate much tall flowering vegetation, butterflies and reptiles requiring open conditions and birds requiring scrub, unless they can survive in other parts of the wood where management is maintaining young growth. Secondly, health and safety issues may arise if you have to deal with hazardous trees and dead snags as the wood self-thins and ages. Lastly, you could be very unlucky if whole areas are flattened by a severe storm, creating uniformity all over again: this would not be the case if a range of age-classes and species is maintained, as young growth has a smaller 'sail area' and is less susceptible to storm damage. Having said this, some non-intervention areas in parts of the wood will be very valuable for species requiring old-growth conditions.

habitat requirements. For the remainder of this chapter we will consider some important biodiversity features associated with different silvicultural systems.

3.3 **Coppice**

Coppicing – a likely evolutionary response to the wounding of trees by browsing animals, uprooting by storms or fire – arises from the activation of dormant buds at the base of the stem, or from the formation of buds on callus tissue at the cut surface (as in beech). With repeated cutting at the base of the stem, coppice stools are formed from which the new stems arise. New shoots also arise from root suckers in poplar, aspen, wild cherry, elm and alder. These can produce clonal masses that may come to dominate large parts of a wood. Most other broadleaved species, such as oak, hornbeam, lime and sweet chestnut withstand repeated coppicing well; but ash, birch, sycamore and beech are usually less long-lived as coppice.

In its basic form, coppice is grown as an even-aged crop, known as simple coppice which is a form of 'low forest', never obtaining its maximum height (Figure 3.2). From a biodiversity viewpoint, its underlying problem is that it produces almost uniform young growth with an homogeneous vertical structure: there are no trees in older age classes and often little deadwood (except that present in old coppice stools). This uniformity is further emphasised if, as in many stands, your wood has been neglected for 50 years or more, or the coppice is dominated by a single species such as sweet chestnut. This can be partially remedied if the coppice is grown in two- or multi-layered systems with mature standard trees (the latter often

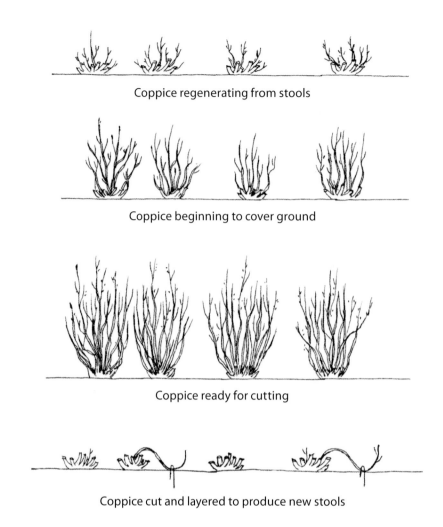

Coppice regenerating from stools

Coppice beginning to cover ground

Coppice ready for cutting

Coppice cut and layered to produce new stools

Figure 3.2 Simple coppice system, producing uniformly young, even-aged growth on rotations of usually less than 30 years.

self-seeded or planted) in a coppice-with-standards system. These standard trees provide an additional range of age-classes, and ideally should themselves be uneven-aged in order to maximise structural benefits.

In coppice-with-standards, the standard trees were traditionally grown on multiples of the coppice rotation, usually up to 4–5r (where r = a coppice rotation), the numbers roughly halving with each progressive age cohort. Their density was a compromise between the productivity of the two components of the crop: in the pre-War era a 50:50 cover of each component, coppice and standards, was considered a normal stocking for working coppices, with a minimum of 25 standards per hectare. A very low stocking of standard trees, covering only 10–15% of the area, is recommended by Butterfly Conservation, in order to encourage a range of butterflies and moths between coppice rotations (Clarke *et al.*, 2011). In practice many neglected small woods now contain high densities of veteran standard trees that were never thinned in the past and so effectively shaded out the coppice layer, while in other cases the coppice itself has grown into an even-aged high forest. Both states create the shady conditions that have led to widely-publicised losses of specialist species associated with young growth, including migrant warblers, nightjars, dormice and fritillary butterflies.

If your wood contains significant areas of coppice, there are a number of remedial actions that you can undertake to diversify the coppice area and increase its attractiveness to wildlife. At the level of the whole wood, options which you might consider are:

- In simple coppice such as sweet chestnut, introduce some standard trees, up to densities of 25 per hectare, to vary the canopy structure. When they grow into mature oaks these could occupy 20–40% of the overhead cover, although a lower cover density may be appropriate to encourage butterfly species. Standards can be promoted by singling some coppice stools for native species (i.e. reducing them to one stem), or by planting and natural regeneration. Species with relatively open canopies, such as oak, ash and birch, will allow more light through.

- Avoid a monoculture: increase the proportion of other site-native trees and shrubs, which may need to be introduced if natural regeneration sources are too far distant. In chestnut coppice, stools can be 'thinned' using brushwood killers, stump removal or premature cutting to prevent rapid re-growth. If the stand is to be promoted to high forest, felling and 'singling' stools can be used to create space for other species already present, or group felling and restocking practised. The overall diversity of different species groups using the canopy should increase in proportion to the greater variety of host species and the more diverse canopy structure.
- Intervene to favour species other than the dominant one, be it hazel, sweet chestnut or hornbeam, by selective thinning after coppicing and before canopy closure. Allow the species composition to diversify naturally over time through natural regeneration.
- You may not be able to cope with coppicing more than one part of the wood on a strict rotational basis. In the most difficult and inaccessible areas, therefore, consider allowing some areas to revert to high forest, where they will self-thin and begin to follow a natural dynamic.
- Retain all old or veteran trees (including standards, if present) in order to boost the deadwood supply and to encourage hole-nesting birds and bats.

At the level of the felling unit, compartment or cant:

- Vary the coppice coupe size, with some larger areas of 0.5–1 ha if your wood will accommodate them, to encourage woodland birds and small mammals.
- Maintain wide rides and glades (see Section 4.1) to provide open conditions and links between cut areas for species that require more light.
- Revert to a continuous-cover or group selection felling regime in the less economically viable parcels, or non-intervention as above.

Woodland owner coppicing hazel in winter.

Restoring neglected coppice

If your coppice area has been long neglected, and you have reason to believe that there are species in your wood, or nearby, that might benefit from access to young growth stages, you could consider trying to reinstate the coppice cycle.

Cutting affects the hormonal balance of the tree, promoting the breaking of dormant lateral buds that were formed at the base of the young shoots while they were developing. Provided cutting is repeated at regular intervals, these buds will continually re-form and the stools will remain viable for many cycles. In ancient woods, large ash, hazel and lime stools are frequently hundreds of years old, and in some rarer cases are thought to be over a thousand years. A proportion, however, will die of natural causes at each cutting (5–10% mortality may be typical for mature stools (Evans, 1984; Harmer and Howe, 2003)) but they

Coppice management myths

Coppice management is fairly straightforward – regular cutting results in fresh re-growth. No thinning is usually necessary, as competition between shoots on the same coppice stool rapidly reduces their number to a few dominant shoots. Being an ancient tradition, several theories have grown up around the silviculture and management of coppicing that have yet to be rigorously tested. Harmer and Howe (2003) and Harmer (2004) have examined evidence for the effectiveness of different cutting treatments using practical investigations and literature accounts:

Quality of cut – sloping cuts are often advocated, preferably south-facing in order to dry quickly and to prevent rot. While it is possible that cutting on the slant increases the area of the wound and the chance of callus bud formation, there is little convincing evidence that sloping cuts on coppice stools produce better results than flat ones. An early experiment on chestnut with different billhook, bow-saw or chainsaw cuts also failed to show differences in subsequent height growth.

Position of cut – low cuts are considered best, presumably because the developing shoots are then encouraged to develop their own root systems. Higher cuts tend to produce more shoots in some experiments, although these stems may then be less stable compared with those arising from low cuts, and there is some evidence that they may be more prone to butt rot.

Season of coppicing – the conventional view is that coppice is best cut during the dormant period, between late autumn and early spring, as there will be less bark tearing, stump mortality and frost damage to developing shoots. Such timing also avoids the peak of the bird nesting period from April to July. However, experimental coppicing out of season, in late summer and early autumn, has shown little difference in shoot numbers and height growth after a few years growth, compared with conventional 'in season' cutting. Some authorities claim that summer-cut coppice poles are more prone to deterioration and decay than winter-cut material.

Protection of coppice stools – if deer or rabbits are a problem in your wood, they will certainly target any young coppice re-growth: some protection will be needed for 2–3 years to prevent the stools from being repeatedly stripped and possibly killed. Conservationists often advocate barricading the coppice stools with brash piles, sometimes topped with bramble and rose briar, or 'dead hedges' consisting of brash interwoven between upright stakes. However, brash piles seem to be particularly ineffective in preventing damage, unless a robust dead hedge surround is constructed: ultimately fencing or culling may be required.

can be replaced, through planting, natural regeneration or layering. In neglected stands, the dormant basal buds become progressively embedded in bark as the stem diameter increases, gradually reducing their ability to re-shoot over time. The critical interval varies considerably between species and site factors, such as shading and site fertility, may also play a part. While there is no doubt that the vigour of reshooting of many tree species declines and the mortality of stumps increases with increasing stool age and size, there is no compelling quantitative or predictive evidence for different species. Some conservation authorities argue that after only 50 years it is not worth re-coppicing neglected stands, but this judgement is often based more on the consideration that the open character of coppice and some of its associated wildlife may have been lost, rather than its inherent re-coppicing ability.

Even if the coppice has reverted to high forest, some species, such as hornbeam, sweet chestnut, field maple, lime and ash, may recover from cutting well, but expect poor results with subjects such as beech and birch. You can experiment by cutting a small group of stools at an edge, where there is plenty of light. One technique to try is selective coppicing – that is, removing the largest coppice stems, but leaving one or two subordinate stems to maintain supplies of carbohydrate to the stool during its recovery. If sufficient new shoots develop, the remaining subordinate stems can be removed after two to three years and the rotation re-established. Even if recovery is poor, there are some advantages in this as sparse stool densities will provide additional structural diversity and encourage natural regeneration of other species through seeding. Similar approaches are used for restoring ancient pollards in wood-pasture (see Section 4.3).

Creating new coppice stools and pollards

Creating new coppice stools and pollards is a much easier task than restoring ancient ones. Most native broadleaves will form stools if cut as early as the first growing season, but for good coppicing species such as ash, hazel and oak, the cut can be deferred for up to 20 years. A serviceable rule of thumb states that the first cut should be made at half the eventual coppice age, but in the case of beech and birch, the earlier the cut, the more likely there will be successful re-growth. New pollards can also be successfully created on young trees up to 15 cm in diameter and up to 15 years old. These are best situated in open positions along the edge of the wood, or along a ride. For species like ash and beech, Read (2000) recommends making the initial cut above the eventual pollard height of 2–3 m, leaving some lower branches intact while new re-growth takes place on the bole, then finally removing these lower branches, leaving stubs where new shoots will arise.

3.4 Even-aged plantations

Nearly 70% of the woodland area in Britain consists of recent plantations, and more than half of these are coniferous, with a much higher proportion of conifers in Wales and Scotland than in England. If you have inherited a plantation, the chances are that whole sections or compartments will be even-aged: all trees were planted (or rarely naturally regenerated) at the same time and were progressively thinned with the intention of clear felling and replacing the stand at the end of the rotation. The overriding advantage of the system is that uniform crops are produced, with economies of scale achieved through planting, thinning and felling large areas of similar crops. However, as we have seen, the prospects for wildlife are poor because of the uniformity of these often monospecific, mono-layered and even-aged canopies. In mid-rotation in particular, little light penetrates through managed plantation canopies and, except at edges and rides, there will be an almost complete lack of understorey trees and shrubs, and sometimes very little ground flora. Non-native conifer plantations of spruce, Western hemlock and Douglas fir cast an all-year-round shade and can quickly impoverish spring flowers such as bluebells and wood anemones.

Woodland owner discusses management options for a PAWS woodland with a Forestry Commission advisor.

Restoring conifer plantations on ancient woodland sites

Many plantations have been sited on upland grazing or ex-arable land, so it will take a very long time before they begin to develop recognisable woodland communities. However, the policy of 'improving' existing woods that prevailed for 50 years from the 1930s to the mid-1980s, resulted in about 40% of ancient woods, over 220,00 ha, being felled and replanted with more productive, even-aged conifer or broadleaved tree crops. Through forest policy initiatives and grant-aid, many of these plantations on ancient woodland sites (PAWS) are now being restored or reverted to their former semi-natural state: the best techniques for doing this are still being worked out.

The first step, if you own a plantation, is to check whether indeed it is a PAWS candidate. There is plenty of guidance published by the Forestry Commission and Woodland Trust on how to survey and restore PAWS sites (Thompson et al., 2003; The Woodland Trust, 2005) but it is worth first checking the Ancient Woodland Inventory maps to see if your wood is listed (or indeed whether parts are semi-natural, ancient woodland). The Inventory originally covered only woods of 2 ha or larger, but in some counties re-surveying has recently increased the resolution down to 0.25 ha.

If your wood is ancient, it should be possible to confirm this by searching for remnant features of the original wood, including the following:

- Deadwood: the presence of felled trees, branch debris, stumps and coppice stools from the previous woodland cover.
- Archaeological features such as wood banks, saw-pits, drainage grips, charcoal hearths, pollards and stubs.
- Native woodland species that are not part of the plantation crop, including shrubs and ground flora, and buried seed in the soil.

In the last case, there may be scattered native tree survivors that have become engulfed by the plantation canopy, including former coppice stools and veterans, but which may be salvageable. In windthrown gaps willows, birches and ash will often have self-seeded and there may be lingering patches of hazel, holly, hawthorn and other shrubs present in the understorey. Perhaps the best indicators of woodland origin are the so-called group of ancient woodland indicator plants, mainly ground flora species that are poor colonisers and are therefore largely restricted to these sites (see Section 2.1). Lists of these indicators are available from the literature (e.g. Rose, 2006) and local wildlife trusts, and include species like bluebell, wood anemone, ramsons and yellow archangel (see also Table 2.1). Remember that one bluebell does not make an ancient woodland – rather it requires a number of indicator species, occurring consistently within a stand, to confirm the diagnosis.

If you have found these features in your wood, the next stage is to plan a restoration strategy. Essentially, this involves thinning the plantation canopy with a view to eventually – perhaps in the very long-term – replacing it with native species, if possible using plant materials already present on site. To make a start, conventional advice is to thin selectively around native trees where they survive (including old pollards and coppice stools), as well as where 'hotspots' of remnants of old woodland and regeneration occur, such as along rides and streamsides (Figure 3.3). Once this holding operation has been achieved, the next question is whether, and how quickly to convert the plantation to a more semi-natural state. As every wood is different, there are no hard and fast rules, but points to consider are:

- How much of the original plantation to retain. Generally speaking, retained areas of mature canopy, even non-native conifers, can benefit species that thrive in shade or use the canopy for protection. If reserved in non-intervention areas, they will also provide an accumulating source of deadwood. Furthermore, there is little point in prioritising conversion treatments in parts of the wood conspicuously lacking in remnant features: partial restoration of the most promising areas may be the best solution.
- Similarly, numbers of native trees surviving amongst the canopy may be too sparse to provide sufficient natural regeneration, even after thinning of the main crop. Some lowland conifer plantations contain only 10–100 individuals per hectare of these survivors, with few viable native saplings and seedlings present on the ground. Such areas can either be left to diversify naturally, or thinned heavily in stages for eventual underplanting (enrichment planting) with native species.
- Heavy thinning of the canopy risks windthrow, both to the plantation crop and any native remnants that have suddenly been exposed. It should be avoided on exposed sites or where the soils are shallow or prone to waterlogging: spruces, Douglas fir and Western hemlock maybe particularly susceptible on such sites.
- Thinning may also stimulate heavy weed growth which can swamp young regeneration and in turn encourage heavy browsing if deer and rabbits are abundant. Conversely, prolific regeneration of the non-native canopy species (e.g. pine, spruce, fir, Western hemlock and sycamore) can occur and may need to be controlled. Thinning intensity will clearly influence the response of competitors such as bramble, bracken and grasses. Some experiments have shown that after very heavy (80%) thinning of Corsican pine on lowland sites, bramble thickets approaching to a metre tall developed after four years compared with less than half a metre in light (20%) thinning. Nevertheless light thinning did not allow tree seedlings to establish any better, indicating that gradual removal of the crop, often advocated, may not necessarily be more effective than rapid clearance.

3.5 Converting conifer and broadleaf plantations to uneven-aged systems

At this point we can consider different silvicultural systems which may be used to restore even-aged woodlands, both on PAWS sites, and in more recent woodland. The flow diagram (Figure 3.4) presents a choice between gradual, phased removal of the existing canopy versus very heavy thinning and rapid removal. Phased removals have the attraction of

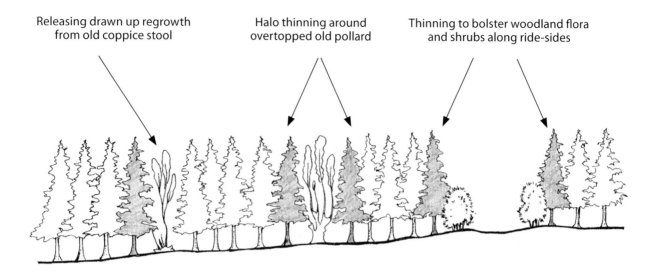

Releasing drawn up regrowth from old coppice stool

Halo thinning around overtopped old pollard

Thinning to bolster woodland flora and shrubs along ride-sides

Figure 3.3 Recovering semi-natural features from a PAWS woodland site by carefully targeting removals of the plantation trees (shown shaded), (after Woodland Trust, 2005).

avoiding severe disruption to any wildlife present such as bats and dormice, fungi and insects requiring deadwood substrate under shady, moist conditions, as well avoiding damage to young regeneration and ground vegetation. The most appropriate techniques here are to develop shelterwoods based on selection and group selection silviculture – i.e. continuous cover systems. On the other hand, if thinning the crop is likely to cause windthrow, or access is difficult and browsing pressure is likely to be a problem, rapid conversion using clear felling may be more feasible, followed by fencing and replanting. If windthrow is not thought too risky, a uniform shelterwood system can be used, supplementing any young regeneration by underplanting with native trees and shrubs where necessary.

Rapid conversion using the uniform system normally involves the removal of up to a third of the mature canopy cover, leaving a shelterwood of 75–120 trees per hectare if light-demanding trees are to be regenerated or planted, or more dense (150–200 trees per hectare) for shade-bearers. To avoid heavy weed growth suppressing seedlings, regeneration or replanting should be as rapid as possible – perhaps 5–10 years under Scots pine, but up to 20–30 years for oak and beech, with progressive removal of the canopy (Figure 3.5).

Continuous cover forestry regimes are becoming more popular in Britain. About 30,000 ha (3–4%) of the Forestry Commission estate are now earmarked as non-clear felling systems, and in Wales the National Assembly recommended that at least 50% of state-owned woodlands should be managed as low-impact silvicultural systems or continuous cover. For woodland owners considering certification, the UK Woodland Assurance Scheme recommends that in windfirm (conifer) plantations *"lower impact silvicultural systems shall be increasingly favoured where they are suited to the site and species"* unless *"there is evidence that clear-felling provides habitat that has a high value for biodiversity"* (UKWAS, 2012).

A number of practical and ecological drawbacks of continuous cover forestry need to be carefully weighed beforehand. To develop an intimate mixture of trees sizes requires careful management and stocktaking, and very long timescales to achieve the desirable uneven-aged structure (Figure 3.6). The inherent lack of uniformity means that forestry operations would be scattered over a wide scale and that felling and extraction difficulties around young regeneration will be acute. Control of browsing is difficult, as there is good protection and cover for deer, etc. The windthrow risk is high, except on well-drained soils, because the openings made in the canopy by felling are proportionally larger than in conventional, low-thinning operations.

Technical guides are available on how to set about the conversion (e.g. Kerr, 2008), but the overall aim is to produce a skewed distribution of size classes with small-sized individuals the

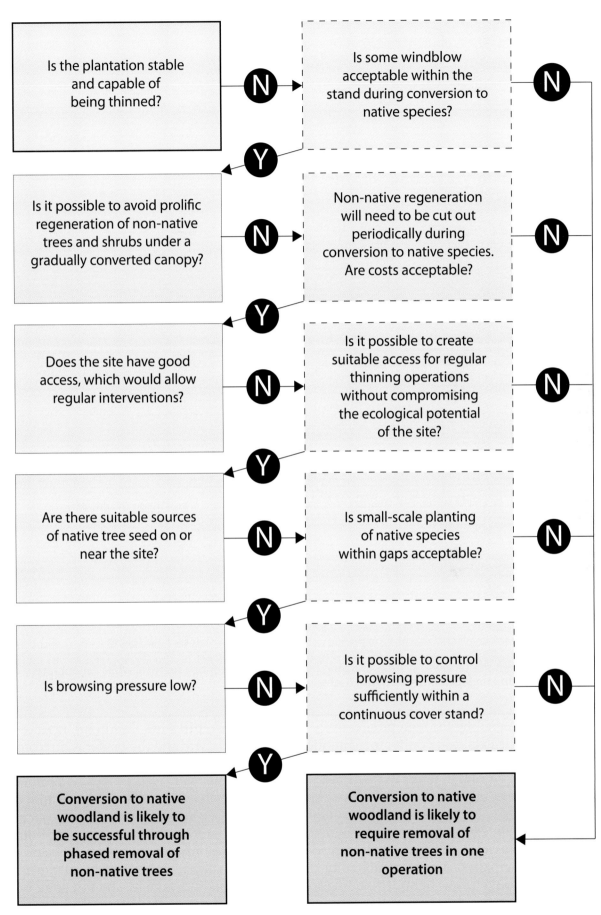

Figure 3.4 Decision pathways for restoring PAWS woodland using phased or rapid removal of the original crop (from Thompson *et al.*, 2003).

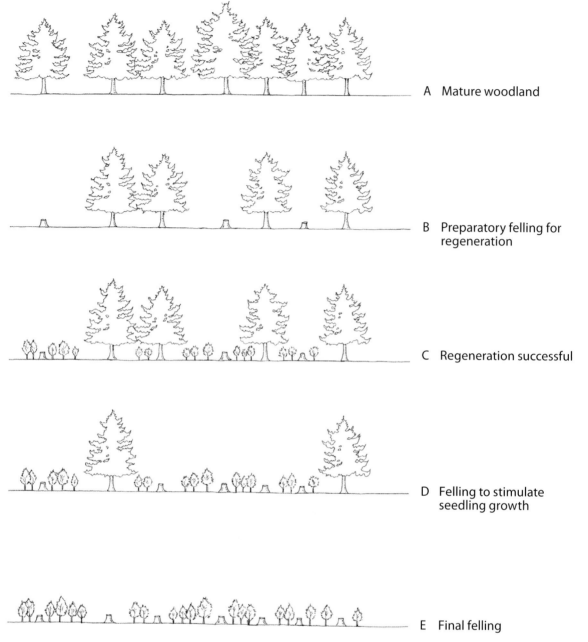

A   Mature woodland

B   Preparatory felling for regeneration

C   Regeneration successful

D   Felling to stimulate seedling growth

E   Final felling

Figure 3.5 Uniform shelterwood system, showing the sequence of canopy removal while regenerating or replanting a young replacement wood with native species.

most frequent, grading through progressively larger size classes to a few dominant, mature individuals. The details are rather too complicated to go into here and the reader is directed to the excellent technical guides produced by the Forestry Commission and the Continuous Cover Forestry Group. In terms of the timescale, to convert an even-aged 10 ha wood to continuous cover might take 80 years, assuming it is regenerated in small groups of 0.15 ha. Regenerating 10% of the area would therefore mean felling seven such groups at eight year intervals (Harris, 2009). Many woods smaller than this will not be able to support the full range of size classes, or if this were attempted there would be only very limited patches of each cohort, perhaps too small a habitat for certain species specialising in a particular growth stage. There would be few light-demanding species able to take advantage, unless a good ride network or open space is also present. One approach would be to work with neighbouring woodland owners to achieve this type of structure over a larger area, with economies of scale in harvesting.

3.6 The harvesting commitment of different silvicultural options in small woods

The choice of silvicultural system and the size of the felling unit or coupe adopted both have profound implications for small woodlands. If a small-group felling system over extended rotations is adopted with the goal of creating an uneven-aged tree population, including large, old trees, the annual commitment will not be great and the intervals between interventions will be long. In contrast, maintaining a regular coppicing cycle is a heavy commitment because of the short rotation, even though this may be desirable in the interests of promoting certain woodland birds or butterflies.

Table 3.2 summarises the situation for a small woodland of 3 ha, managed under different systems. If the felling unit is 0.15 ha, this will allow 20 such units to be fitted in. The example shows that cutting hazel coppice on a seven year rotation would require the clearance of up to three 0.15 ha units per year in order to promote the full age range of 0–7 years throughout the wood. If the coppice is hornbeam, sweet chestnut or ash, the rotation could well be 20–30 years, which obviously decreases the frequency of cutting. This also has the effect of staggering the age interval between different cohorts, a situation that might no longer suit a relatively immobile species needing to colonise freshly cut areas that are immediately adjacent.

In theory, high forest systems require fewer management interventions because they operate on much longer rotations than coppice. For a group selection system, based on a larger felling unit of 0.25 ha and with a turnover of 80–100 years, the felling interval compared with coppice increases to 6.3–8.3 years in this example. This has a number of attractions as there would be a greater range of age-classes, giving a structure that is closer to the natural state (as we saw at the beginning of this chapter), while requiring less frequent management on the whole. At the same time as felling the prescribed area, other operations might be necessary in other parts of the wood, such as planting areas that do not regenerate satisfactorily or thinning the older units with a view to selecting a good final

A   Before felling mature tree

B   After felling mature tree

Figure 3.6 Continuous cover silviculture using the selection system, in which individual trees or very small groups are felled at maturity, creating small gaps for regeneration.

timber crop. These longer rotations are not compatible with the specialist species of young coppice, although using group selection in this case would still produce considerable areas of young growth. In this example, between a fifth and a tenth of the woodland area would still be relatively open, in the pre-canopy closure stage, while at the same time significantly increasing the opportunities for species requiring mature growth stages.

A final option shown in Table 3.2 is the continuous cover system. There is no requirement here to set a felling unit size, as individual and small groups of trees are felled throughout the whole wood, traditionally at intervals of 6–10 years, during which any necessary thinning operations are also carried out. The aim is to select the best trees for sawlogs, which can extend rotations for 125 years or longer, although the criterion is the size (diameter) of the tree rather than its age.

There are of course many alternative strategies that a woodland owner can adopt other than those presented above. If the commitment is too great, you can simply confine operations to parts of the wood where access and extraction are easiest, allowing the remainder to develop into overmature woodland with minimum or irregular interventions. If you have neighbours, you may be able to agree a management regime for the whole wood that optimises its potential for wildlife, for example by coordinating coppicing efforts to maintain adjacent areas of young growth, or consolidating non-intervention stands in other parts. Much will depend on the wildlife survey (Chapter 2) and an appraisal of the potential of the wood to serve particular species groups.

3.7 Ash dieback (*Hymenoscyphus fraxineus*)

Chalara dieback of ash is a serious fungal disease (*Hymenoscyphus fraxineus*) which causes a vascular disease resulting in leaf wilt, crown dieback and bark lesions, and in many cases the death of the infected tree. It was first identified in Poland in 1992 and has since spread across Europe. Twenty years later it was found in a consignment of trees in a British nursery, originally imported from continental Europe. Since its discovery it has been found in nurseries, recently planted woodland and older, established woodland across Great Britain, particularly in the east. The infection of older trees suggests that the disease might have also entered Great Britain by natural means. Trees of all ages can be affected, but tree death is particularly common in saplings. Mature trees infected with *H. fraxineus* tend to succumb more readily to secondary pathogens, such as *Armillaria*.

How to identify trees affected by *Hymenoscyphus fraxineus*
Symptoms may be visible on leaves, shoots, stems and branches of trees affected by *H. fraxineus*. In younger trees, much of the crown may show the loss of leaves, or dieback.

Table 3.2
Management commitments resulting from a) the choice of silvicultural system, and b) the size of the felling unit in a small wood of 3 ha.

Silvicultural system	Rotation length (yr)	Felling unit size (ha)	No. of working units	Felled units per year	Mean annual cut (ha)	Cutting interval
Coppice, short rotation	7			2.86	0.43	every year
Coppice, medium rotation	20–30	0.15	20	1.0–0.6	0.15–0.10	1–1.5 years
Group selection	80–100	0.25	12	0.16–0.12	0.04–0.03	6.3–8.3 years
Continuous cover	125	-	-	-	-	6–10 years

Epicormic shoots may develop on branches and the trunk of affected trees. Look out for:

- Foliage: wilting leaves and black/brownish discolouration that extends to the midrib and leaf stalk.
- Branches and stems: diamond-shaped lesions on stems and branches which are centred on a dead side shoot. Lesion-girdling causes wilting and dieback of shoots and branches, particularly in the upper crown. Underneath the lesions, infected wood may be strongly stained, with the stain extending longitudinally beyond the dead bark.
- Whole tree: extensive shoot, twig and branch dieback on severely infected trees, often accompanied by epicormic shoot proliferation below the trunk lesion.

The disease spreads by airborne spores that are believed to disperse over tens of kilometres. The movement of infected plant material, such as saplings, increases the risk of spread over greater distances. Images and videos of symptoms can be viewed on the Forestry Commission website (www.forestry.gov.uk/chalara).

Managing infected trees

Suspect trees should be reported to the Forestry Commission Tree Alert page (www.forestry.gov.uk/treealert). No further action may be necessary, unless a Plant Health Notice is served that requires action. In new native woods where large numbers of ash trees are affected, hygiene measures may be impractical, and the trees left *in situ*. It is possible that resistant trees might be identified in such circumstances, and natural regeneration from these resistant trees could form part of a long-term solution. Particularly for important veteran individuals and old pollards, local burning, burying or composting of fallen leaves might help to reduce the rate of spread of the disease. For more detailed information and the most recent management guidance, visit the Forestry Commission website (www.forestry.gov.uk/chalara). Felling or coppicing is not normally recommended, as some trees may be naturally resistant – only if the aim is to reduce infection pressure on a site should heavily infected trees be removed on a case-by-case individual basis.

Some owners of new native woodland may be tempted to remove infected or recently planted ash trees and replant with other species, especially if a large number of trees are affected. In most cases, this will not be necessary. Some 'natural' thinning by the disease may provide valuable open areas in new native woods, slowing down the shading of rides and glades. However, for certain grant aided woods, owners should check whether the option of leaving some areas open would be allowed within the grant scheme, or whether restocking is eligible for grant support. Grants may be available to replace infected trees with other species: inquire with your local Forestry Commission or Forest Service Northern Ireland office, or visit their websites, for advice on whether there are grants available for your particular needs. If replanting is undertaken, it might be an opportunity to look again at the original planting mix, and introduce some diversity into the tree planting, or to plant shrubs to improve the structural diversity of the wood. Alternative native broadleaved species have been suggested by Natural England (http://publications.naturalengland.org.uk/publication/5273931279761408) including aspen, beech, birch, cherry, field maple, hornbeam, oak, lime and rowan. Sycamore and other non-natives should not be planted within SSSIs or other conservation sites.

Dieback in ash resulting from other causes

Symptoms of other diseases and conditions can be mistaken for infection by *H. fraxineus*:

- Frost and drought can cause similar wilting and dieback symptoms to *H. fraxineus*. Consideration of the time of year and weather conditions may help to eliminate these as a cause.
- Dieback symptoms on ash can be caused by physical disorders, such as root disturbance, although trees may show signs of recovery under these circumstances.

4 Improving woodland habitat for wildlife

4.1 Woodland edge and open space

Internal rides, glades and other open spaces are very important structural elements within woodland, providing valuable habitat for a wide range of wildlife, much of which differs from the high forest areas. A diverse range of sun-loving plants, insects and reptiles benefit from sunny open areas, often reminiscent of communities in unimproved grassland, heathland or other open habitats. In contrast, other insects, plants, birds and mammals benefit from the woodland edge, which is essentially the interface between the high forest and open ground (Figure 4.1). In many conifer plantations on ancient woodland sites, the only native shrubs and trees remaining might be found along the margins of rides and glades.

In some woods, well-developed rides and glades will already exist, and just require continued management. In others, these open areas may have closed over and require some management intervention such as coppicing or clearing. If you own a wood with little or no open space, or one in which there are legal restrictions on widening existing 'narrow' rides, there may also be opportunities to create a new glade.

Layout of rides and glades

Rides are tracks or corridors of open space, which include all the area between the trees on either side. They provide access to the woodland on foot or with vehicles, and are extremely valuable for wildlife. They are not bridle paths. Rides which meander through a wood, rather like a river, are good for wildlife because of the variety of sunny aspects they contain, and the shelter they afford. This is preferable to the straight corridors found in some forestry plantations, which tend to act as a wind tunnel. With existing straight rides, wind funnelling may be reduced by creating 'pinch points' to baffle the wind, or by angling the start and finish of the ride, close to the edge of the wood. Occasional standard trees retained in the centre of a ride will also baffle wind flows. Creating a series of bays or scallops along a ride will also have a similar effect, both disrupting wind flow and providing shelter (Figure 4.2). Scallops will increase the length of the ride edge, the foliage available to insects, and hence the insect biomass for foraging birds and bats. Scallops also enhance habitat diversity by increasing the area of tall herbs and providing more

Figure 4.1 Profile of a structurally diverse, graduated woodland edge found along glades and rides.

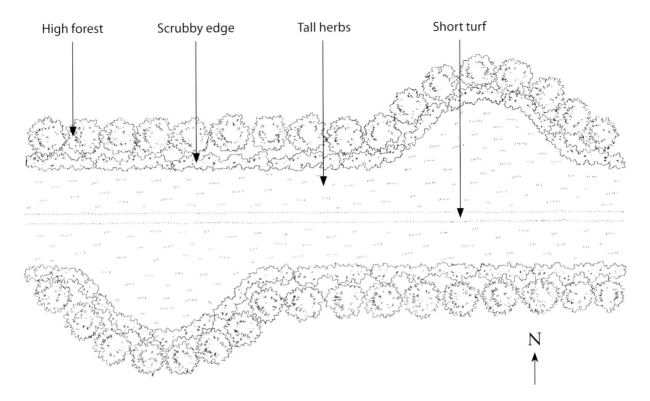

High forest   Scrubby edge   Tall herbs   Short turf

N

Figure 4.2 Aerial view of a linear ride to show how scallops may be positioned.

extensive areas of scrub along the woodland edge, particularly bramble and blackthorn thickets. They may be 30–50 m long and 10–20 m deep, but these dimensions can vary.

Glades can also provide excellent habitat for wildlife, and may include more open ground habitat than rides. These are non-linear, permanently open areas, with few or no trees. One advantage of glades is that larger patches of habitat can be maintained, including more substantial areas of scrub along the woodland edge. Glades are usually incorporated into the ride network, for example at the intersection of two rides (Figure 4.3) but may also be isolated (Figure 4.4). Felling one or more corners around a ride intersection is probably the easiest way of creating and maintaining glades, whilst also enabling wildlife to disperse along the ride network to reach the glade.

Creating new open space

If your woodland lacks good quality open space and edge habitat, some clearance work can be undertaken in both broadleaved and coniferous woodland, including areas of high forest and coppice. However, you should not clear significant areas of woodland, particularly on ancient woodland sites without asking several important questions, including:

- Is the wood a compartment of a larger block of woodland which already has good quality open space? In which case, though it may be an attractive option to create rides and glades, this would not necessarily add to the overall quality of the larger woodland habitat, and might possibly be detrimental to wildlife.
- Was the wood formerly wood pasture, maintained by grazing? If so, some clearance for grazing might be considered (see Section 4.2 and the *Management of ancient wood pasture* (Forestry Commission Scotland, 2009).
- Would any clearance work disturb or destroy existing high forest habitat of high biodiversity value? For example, could this disturb rare woodland plants, old canopy trees, rare insect communities of damp, shady conditions or destroy areas of dense understorey supporting rare woodland specialists such as Bechstein's bat.

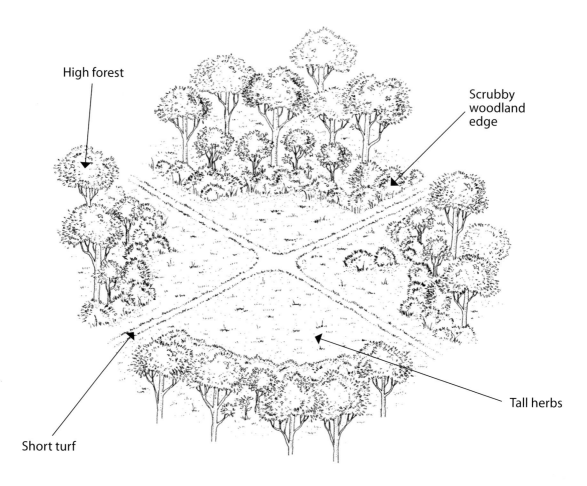

High forest

Scrubby woodland edge

Tall herbs

Short turf

Figure 4.3 A large glade created at the intersection of two rides.

Figure 4.4 Isolated glade in a conifer plantation.

If the answer to all of these questions is no, then it may be possible to open the canopy to enhance the woodland habitat.

Managing rides and glades

The key to managing rides and glades for wildlife is to maintain open, sunny conditions and a structurally diverse, shrubby woodland edge. A ride or glade needs to be wide enough to allow sunlight to reach the central area as well as the south-facing shrubby edge; east-west orientated rides provide the greatest variety of site conditions between the north and south aspects. For this reason, east-west rides should be at least one and a half times wider than the height of the trees on the south side, which is likely to be at least 25 m in deciduous high forest, less in coppice. The south-facing woodland edge of a ride orientated east-west will be warm in the summer sunshine, whilst the north facing edge will be cooler and damper. Both aspects are important for insects; the sunny edge supporting basking insects and the shady edge more attractive to feeding insect larvae. The width can be proportionally less in coppiced or younger woodland that has not achieved its full height, but will need widening as the trees grow taller. If an existing ride or glade is not wide enough, it may be extended slowly over a period of several years. It is important not to lose valuable habitat such as a scrubby woodland edge, rare species or older trees which support species of conservation concern, such as rare insects. Some rides therefore may not be suitable for widening. North-south rides receive less sunlight, and host a flora and fauna more characteristic of light woodland shade, thus providing important habitat in their own right.

Rides are typically managed as a two- or three-zone system. The three-zone system (Figure 4.5), which gives more variety for wildlife, includes:

- a central zone of short turf
- swards of tall herbs and grasses bordering the central zone
- an outer zone of scrub, allowed to develop into dense thickets in places, grading into the high forest.

You can manage glades in a similar way. Trees along the woodland edge may be thinned to create a more graduated edge, and to allow light to penetrate further into the canopy (Figure 4.1). In the high forest ride illustrated (Figure 4.5), the central zone should be a minimum of 2 m wide to allow access to machinery for ride maintenance. In smaller woods where space is more limiting, you can reduce rides to two zones, comprising the central area of short turf and an outer zone of predominantly tall herbs and grasses, with small patches of light scrub. These rides can still be beneficial, but the lack of a good scrubby woodland edge makes them less attractive than wider, three-zone rides.

Rides and glades must be actively managed to prevent the edges advancing and scrub growth developing into woodland, and to maintain the diversity and quality of the habitat mosaic. This involves mowing herbaceous vegetation and coppicing or clearing scrub. You should vary the timing and frequency of cutting of different sections of a ride, and the zones within rides and glades, to increase their value for wildlife, but this may depend to some extent on practical and economic considerations. The central zone of a ride for example should be mown at least once, or possibly twice a year to maintain the short turf. Any areas of bare ground caused by machinery will add to the value of this habitat. Cut up to 25% of the tall herb zone on rotation each year, to create a mosaic of tall herbs of at least four different ages. Ideally, you should undertake this in late July or August to maintain a species-rich sward. In some cases, the results of surveys of the plants and butterflies of woodland rides and glades (see Chapter 2) might be essential to help you get the timing right. Providing the rides are mown in rotation, and only a small area is cut each year, then insect populations in the area as a whole should not be harmed. The cuttings from this will rot down if left, effectively creating a nutrient-rich compost which would encourage rank and weedy

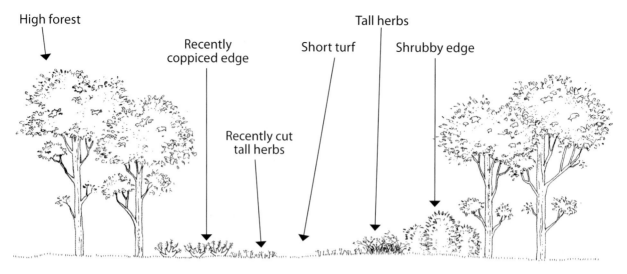

Figure 4.5 Profile of a three-zone ride management system.

vegetation, such as nettles and grasses, while suppressing more desirable species. You should remove these, or at least stack them in one place.

If a ride represents a 'legal boundary', separating ownerships within a larger block of woodland, then some discussion with other woodland owners should result in a joint management plan which enables the ride to be managed appropriately.

The shrubby woodland edge should also be cut, but at less regular intervals, or it will grow up into high forest. Lengths should be cut or coppiced every 8–20 years, to create a mosaic of structural diversity along the edge with panels of different aged shrubs and coppiced trees. Ideally the rotation period should match the point at which an area of scrub has reached the maximum size and density required. You should undertake this work outside the bird nesting season, i.e. between August and late February. Some brash may be retained in localised piles along the woodland edge in the cut areas, as a source of deadwood.

To offer maximum variety to the organisms making use of them, large blocks of even-aged vegetation greater than 50 m or so in length should be avoided in the scrub and tall herb zones; cut areas should be evenly spread out along the ride network, alternating from one side of the ride to the other.

Control of bracken and bramble along the woodland edge

A major problem, when clearing open space for ride widening and glade creation, is invasion by unwanted vegetation such as bracken and bramble. Both of these species are shade-tolerant and thrive at the woodland edge as well as in open conditions, and are only eventually defeated by dense and continuous overhead canopies. They are also extremely effective competitors with grasses, herbs and young trees, taking up water and nutrients, and reducing overall plant diversity. Both can be virtually impenetrable to access: bracken in some parts of Britain may also harbour native ticks that can transmit Lyme disease to humans. Many websites carry information on this disease, including the National Health Service (www.nhs.uk/conditions/Lyme-disease/Pages/Introduction.aspx).

Bracken is a particular problem because its extensive rhizome system stores large quantities of carbohydrate, making it resilient to damage or clearance of the above-ground fronds. It is not palatable to livestock, making it harder to control. Traditionally, trampling by winter-fed cattle on pastures was considered to give some control by weakening the rhizome, but equally overgrazing can encourage bracken by removing its herbaceous competitors. Cutting, hand-pulling, rolling, ploughing and rooting by pigs can all be effective, but none is a comprehensive treatment and all need constant re-application. Cutting or rolling twice a year for at least five years in late June and August, for example, is needed to achieve any useful level of control (Willoughby *et al.*, 2004). If cutting, the first cut should be in mid-June/

July as the plants reach maturity, or later if nesting birds might be present. This should be followed by a second cut in August (about six weeks after the first cut) to remove new fronds stimulated by the first cut, thus further weakening the rhizome. Crushing involves flattening and bruising bracken stems in midsummer, which weakens rhizomes in a similar manner to cutting. The treatment may need to be repeated later in the first year and in subsequent years, to keep on top of the bracken.

The options for herbicide control are now limited, following the ban in 2011 on the use of Asulam, a herbicide formerly preferred for its relatively high specificity. Herbicides such as glyphosate can also be used to control bracken, but extreme care has to be taken to avoid damage to other vegetation if this broad-spectrum herbicide is used. Application rates of 5 l ha-1 have been recommended (Natural England, 2008). Glyphosate should be applied when fronds have expanded, but before die back of the tips, to maximise translocation to the rhizome. It is most suitable for patches of bracken with deep litter, with other plants absent. Woodland owners should be aware that treated bracken can poison livestock, so if you have animals grazing, they should be excluded from a treated area until the bracken has completely senesced or been removed. Follow-up treatment is likely to be necessary, involving either further mechanical or herbicide spot treatments.

Grazing can also keep bracken under control following successful mechanical treatment. Heavy livestock in winter will also control bracken to some extent through trampling and bruising stems, and breaking up litter layers. Animals should be removed in spring to avoid poisoning. For more information on bracken control, see *Bracken Control: A guide to best practice* (SEARS, 2008) and *Bracken Management and Control* (Natural England, 2008).

Bramble is another versatile species that thrives on disturbance, germinating from a large, viable soil seed bank, the established plants spreading rapidly outwards on rooting stems to form clonal patches. The seeds are readily dispersed by birds and small mammals. Bramble is palatable to grazing and browsing animals and, where deer are abundant, it can be almost entirely stripped from the field layer. Where there is little browsing pressure, however, it can develop into thickets in open or half-shaded conditions and is only temporarily suppressed by cutting or flailing. You can achieve longer-term control of bramble and other woody plants such as gorse and rhododendron where they are suppressing other scrub layer vegetation using robust herbicides such as glyphosate and trichlopyr. The usual technique is to first cut back the vegetation, allow recovery and then spray the young regrowth, repeating as necessary on any recovering patches.

Before waging a war of attrition on bracken and bramble, however, it is worth remembering their considerable conservation benefits (see also Chapter 2). Both bracken and bramble provide cover and shelter for nesting birds and protection for small mammals from their predators, as well as a food supply in late summer and autumn. Areas of bracken and scrub, particularly in the uplands, are important breeding and feeding sites for twite, whinchat, stonechat and ring ouzel, where woodland edges may hold common redstart, pied flycatcher and tree pipit. In lowland deciduous woodland, bramble is important for some of the woodland birds in serious decline, such as nightingale and warblers, as well as more common species such as robin and wren. Mechanical clearance of either species during the nesting season should therefore be avoided.

Both bramble and bracken also have strong claims to supporting a variety of insect life. Bracken cover hosts over 40 species of invertebrates. Bramble is the food plant of 61 moths such as buff arches, peach blossom and fox moth and three butterflies; but its overriding importance is the source of nectar provided by the flowers for butterflies, moths, hoverflies, bees, wasps, lacewings and flies.

Bracken provides a substitute woodland canopy for many shade-loving plants, such as bluebells and violets, where the frond density is not too high, and may protect rarer plants from grazing, including autumn crocus, lesser butterfly orchid and chickweed-wintergreen (English Nature 2001). However both bracken and bramble, at high densities, will shade out other species, especially the latter as it retains a leafy cover for much of the year. Young regenerating trees are in danger of being smothered as the fronds collapse, but can be saved by protecting them in tree shelters: weeding around the base is still necessary to prevent competition for water and nutrients. Research has shown that young trees such as oak and beech are susceptible to bramble competition, contrary to the common perception that bramble protects young trees from grazing by deer and domestic stock, although this may hold true for faster growing birches and willows that can quickly penetrate the thicket.

After weighing the arguments, you are likely to conclude that some bracken and bramble cover is good for wildlife, but that very dense patches are best broken up, particularly where they are encroaching on rides and glades. If you use chemicals, bear in mind that broad-spectrum herbicides are unselective and will damage other vegetation. In ancient woodland the best technique is to use localised treatments, for example spot-spraying individual clumps as and when necessary, and in combination with mechanical methods. If you do use chemical control, you should be aware of the code of practice for using plant protection products that came into force in 2006 (Defra, 2006). More recently, the Plant Protection Products (Sustainable Use) Regulations came into force in 2012. Also check the Health and Safety Executive website for updates (http://www.pesticides.gov.uk/guidance/industries/pesticides/topics/using-pesticides/codes-of-practice). The Code of Practice provides practical guidance to professionals on the safe use of plant protection products that meet legal requirements covering their use; practitioners are permitted to work in a different way, providing that way is just as safe.

Open space for species of conservation concern

Where rides or glades are being created for species of conservation concern, such as fritillary butterflies which have precise microhabitat requirements, then it would be advisable to seek advice from local experts. Factsheets on woodland management for habitat specialist butterflies are also available on the Butterfly Conservation website. More detailed information on the ecology and management of rides and glades can be found in the Forestry Commission's *Managing rides, roadsides and edge habitats in lowland forests* (Ferris and Carter, 2000).

4.2 Grazing

In the past, grazing was very much more widespread in our native woodland than it is today. As recently as the mid 18th century, many British woods were grazed to some extent by both wild and domestic animals, but this has declined dramatically since that time. In some parts of Britain, and especially in the uplands, domestic animals still have indiscriminate access to woodlands, but this can lead to considerable damage to ecosystems, for example where high stocking densities of sheep use woodland for shelter. It has even been suggested that the New Forest more closely resembles the 'wildwood' which developed after the last ice age than much of the high forest we see today (Vera, 2000). Despite a widespread reduction in woodland management, principally through the decline in coppicing, some conservationists have suggested that nature conservation is becoming too 'managed'. The restoration of 'naturalistic' grazing and browsing by wild herbivores (Hodder and Bullock, 2009) has been advocated as one means of allowing natural development to take its course, but in many woods this would be prevented by large deer populations. This is also known as 're-wilding', and its popularity as a concept is growing. However, for most small woodland owners, the limited amounts of grazing available under a woodland canopy will probably be insufficient to support high densities of animals. If your wood is large enough, managed or 'conservation' grazing is one possible option.

Deer

Before any additional conservation grazing management is considered, it is first necessary to establish whether deer are present in the woodland, and if so, the impact which these animals are having on woodland structure and species diversity. Deer can strip coppice regrowth and severely limit natural regeneration in any wood by eating the self-seeded saplings, and prevent development of upland birchwoods into native pine or oak woods. Evidence from studies in an Essex woodland supports the notion that increased deer browsing has contributed to the decline of populations of woodland birds such as nightingale and garden warbler (Holt et al., 2010; 2011). Holt et al. (2010) cut plots to produce young coppice regrowth, with deer excluded by fencing from half of these. Nightingales showed a strong preference for the fenced sections in comparison to the grazed controls, spending 69% of their time in the 6% of the study areas protected from deer. Increased deer browsing is also likely to affect Lepidoptera, Heteroptera and other phytophagus invertebrates favouring vegetation in woodland rides and open areas (Buckley and Mills, 2015). Populations of small mammals relying on vegetation, flowers, fruits and seeds, together with their insect biomass might also be adversely affected.

In many cases, deer densities may already be too high – numbers of muntjac and roe deer exceeding one animal per 1–2 ha have been recorded in some British woods – so grazing by domestic animals may not be necessary or desirable. You may not know how abundant deer are in your wood, or which species are present. Estimates can be made by counting faecal pellets in sample plots, either at a single visit (the standing crop method) or by clearing the plots at repeat intervals and measuring accumulation over time (the accumulation rate method). A Forestry Commission Bulletin describes a useful, but rather involved combination plot technique, combining both methods, to estimate deer numbers (Swanson et al., 2008). For identification purposes, deer faecal pellets are usually dark brown/black, cylindrical and pointed at one end. Roe deer pellets are approximately 18 mm long and 14 mm wide; fallow deer pellets are 15–16 mm long and 8–12 mm wide, indented at the blunt end; and muntjac deer pellets are 10–13 mm long and 5–11 mm wide, sometimes pointed at both ends. The results of monitoring should also indicate whether any control measures such as fencing might be necessary, and whether a deer management plan should be undertaken separately from a conservation grazing plan. The *Woodland Grazing Toolkit* (Sumsion and Pollock, 2005) provides useful guidance on preparing a deer management plan, and is available on the Argyll and Bute Council website.

Introducing conservation grazing

Whilst grazing may not be appropriate for many woodland owners, especially those where fencing is not an option, there are woods where it might be seriously considered. Carefully controlled grazing by small numbers of animals can be used to achieve conservation targets such as the maintenance or creation of structural diversity in the understorey and the management of glades. Animals are likely to influence both species and structural diversity in the field layer, understorey and canopy trees, and hence the populations of insects and their predators. The exact outcome depends on many variables, including the type of animal, stocking density (Table 4.1), feeding preference (Table 4.2), and the effects of dunging and trampling. An accumulation of dung in areas where cattle lie up can lead to tall herb vegetation. Trampling can have beneficial effects on coarse grasses, but may adversely affect soil structure in damper areas.

Table 4.1
Effects of differing grazing levels on woodland habitat (after Mitchell and Kirby, 1990).

Level	Effects on woodland habitat
Low	Saplings present; well developed understorey, no browse line; grazing sensitive species such as honeysuckle and bramble present
Moderate	Saplings scarce, signs of grazing and browsing, patches of bare soil
High	Saplings <20 cm tall; distinct browse line, no shrubs; field layer dominated by less palatable species; palatable species inaccessible to herbivores
Excessive	No regeneration; barking; no shrub layer; loss of structural diversity; extensive bare ground and soil disturbance; invasive species colonising

Fallow deer (up to 1 m at shoulder)

Roe deer (up to 75 cm at shoulder)

Muntjac deer (up to 50 cm at shoulder)

Table 4.2
Feeding behaviour of domestic stock (after Mayle, 1999).

	Feeding method	Species selectivity
Cattle	Bulk grazer, tears off vegetation; maintains longer swards (typically 5 cm); ruminant	Low – prefer grasses and forbs, sometimes browse trees and shrubs
Horses and ponies	Bulk grazer, nips vegetation close to ground (swards typically 2 cm); non-ruminant	High – prefer grasses, but also graze forbs and browse range of trees and shrubs
Sheep	Selectively graze vegetation close to ground (minimum sward height 3 cm); non-ruminant	High – often target flowering plants, frequently browse trees and shrubs
Goats	Selective browsers; ruminant	High – frequently browse trees and shrubs
Pigs	Omnivorous; non-ruminant	Low

The high structural variability of different woodland sites, the types of forage present and its palatability, makes it difficult to be precise about what stocking levels can be maintained. In open woods, such as lowland wood pasture, it may be possible to graze one cow or pony per 1–2 ha for ten months of the year without any negative impact; the equivalent of 4–5 sheep per ha. These levels reduce considerably in closed-canopy woods where there is less available ground vegetation and browse material. For example, the range of annual dry matter of ground vegetation for oak woodland is 0.1–1 tonnes per ha, whereas for acid grassland it is 3–5 tonnes per ha (Sumsion and Pollack, 2005). In these circumstances more realistic stocking levels are of the order of one cow per 10–20 ha or one sheep per 2 ha. This highlights the point that most small woods are simply unable to provide enough forage for any number of animals except, perhaps, for very short intervals of the year. If the stocking levels are too high, conservation aims will be heavily compromised because natural regeneration will cease, scrub layers will start to disappear and bark-stripping of coppice stools and trees will become more prevalent.

Levels of stocking that will maintain natural regeneration of trees and shrubs are also subject to great variability, depending on canopy closure, tree species, woodland structure and composition. Historic reconstructions of the grazing regime in the New Forest indicate that natural regeneration could be sustained at quite high combined stocking levels of one cow per 4.5–5 ha, one horse per 9–15 ha and one red or fallow deer per 3–3.5 ha (Flower 1980, Putman 1986). In the uplands, red deer densities up to seven animals per km^2 have allowed sufficient regeneration of native pinewoods (Gill, 2000). For roe deer, impacts on broadleaved regeneration have been reported at densities varying between 4–12 animals per ha. In general, considering that other grazers may be present, very conservative stocking levels (e.g. of less than one cow or 10 sheep per 10 ha of summer grazing) are probably appropriate for conservation grazing, until monitoring confirms any positive or negative impact.

Before any animals are introduced into your woodland, write a management plan which includes a grazing regime. A useful guide to writing a detailed grazing plan is the *Woodland Grazing Toolkit* (Sumsion and Pollock, 2005), which also provides guidance and background on using woodland (rather than wood pasture) for livestock grazing. In small woods, seasonal grazing is likely to be most appropriate. Grazing in spring and summer is generally avoided, because animals may graze on wild flowers that can lead to a reduction in plant species diversity. Insects and their predators are also likely to be adversely affected. Late summer and autumn is often the best time for seasonal grazing, with maximum biomass and the least likelihood of damaging insect populations. Winter grazing can also be considered, particularly where bracken needs to be controlled, but livestock can cause considerable damage to soils in winter, particularly if the ground is wet. Further information and advice on woodland grazing can be obtained from the Grazing Advice Partnership website.

Grazing ancient wood pastures

Ancient woodland pasture was traditionally managed as areas of grassland or heathland with open-grown veteran trees (Section 4.3), providing grazing, fodder and shelter for livestock. If you own a former wood pasture, you have an opportunity to care for an historic landscape, and the veteran trees themselves, which support rare and specialised wildlife. A long-term commitment to carefully managed grazing regimes is essential to maintain and protect wood pasture. Without this, the site would return to native woodland, but providing they are not overstood by other trees, veteran trees can still be protected by gradual halo-thinning. Managing and restoring traditional wood pasture is outside the scope of this book, but detailed guidance can be found in a number of publications such as *Ancient wood pasture in Scotland: classification and management principles* (Holl and Smith, 2002) and *Management of ancient wood pasture* (Forestry Commission Scotland, 2009).

4.3 Conserving veteran trees

The terms 'veteran' and 'ancient' trees have become almost synonymous, but an ancient tree should strictly be defined by its age, and classed as old for its species. A veteran tree by definition has 'veteran features' including cavities containing wood-mould, bark cracks or hollow, rotting limbs, but is not necessarily extremely old. Here we have adopted the term veteran tree, to include all trees with veteran features, irrespective of their age. A veteran tree will provide an almost continuous supply of deadwood in all stages of decay, which is essential for the survival of the rich assemblages of specialist wildlife – saproxylic insects, fungi and lichens that reside in or on them. Even the roots can develop complex fungal communities. The biological, cultural and historical importance of veteran trees is now more widely recognised, helped by a Woodland Trust initiative called the 'Ancient Tree Hunt' that is designed to identify and map all veteran trees in the British Isles.

Veteran trees are typical of old wood pasture and parkland, where as trees age, their growth rate slows and the crown starts to die back. It is quite possible that you may have one or more veteran trees in your wood, particularly if it includes an ancient woodbank. The aging process in wood pasture trees can take many decades, in the absence of competing trees. Veteran trees may also be found in other habitat, such as high forest, hedgerows and riparian woodland along rivers and streams, where old willows still survive as both managed and lapsed pollards. Many veteran trees were once pollarded to avoid browsing damage, by repeatedly cutting back the shoots on short rotations at 2–3 m above ground. Pollards are often found along edges of woodland and wood banks, marking the boundaries of historic ownership. Veteran maidens and coppice stools are also frequently encountered.

Age can be used to compare trees of the same species, but not as a universal guide to identifying veteran trees, as different trees age at different rates. For example birches tend to rot and collapse relatively quickly, so a veteran tree may only be 100 years old, whereas oaks rot from the centre, so veteran trees with hollow trunks may be many hundreds of years old. Some veteran yews are over a thousand years old. Girth offers a good clue to the age of a tree, but this may be strongly influenced by the environment for a given species, so it usually a combination of size and other characters which confirms its status (Table 4.3). Essentially, the more of these features and microhabitats that a tree possesses, the greater the confidence that the tree is a veteran, although care is required because some features might be present on a younger tree, resulting from environmental or human action rather than the aging process.

Managing veteran trees

Veteran trees are found in a wide range of habitats, and differing conditions. Some may have a long history of management, and others may have been managed at one time, but neglected for many years. For these reasons alone, every individual veteran tree is in some way unique. Ideally, the aim of any management intervention such as pollarding should be to prolong

Table 4.3
Summary of the key characteristics of veteran trees.

Characteristic	
Girth	Large for the species concerned
Hollowing	Progressive hollowing in trunk or major limbs important; hollow trunk indicates a tree of great age
Crevices	Under bark and branches
Exposed wood	Caused by bark loss resulting from damage such as loss of a limb
Rot sites	Exposed wood colonised by 'deadwood specialist' fungi and other deadwood species
Rot holes	Rotting creates holes which may be used by insects, birds and bats
Water pockets	Rot holes may naturally fill with water
Deadwood	Large quantity attached in the canopy, or fallen beneath the tree, usually hosting range of specialist deadwood fungi
Fractured stems	Active shoots associated with fractured trunk or limbs, which are decaying
Sap runs	From wound tissue
Fungi	Fruiting bodies of 'deadwood specialist' species
Lichens	Some lichens specialise on veteran trees

the life of the tree, unless tree surgery is required because the tree has become a hazard to people. Veteran trees can also be protected by managing the forest around them. For example, tree roots near the surface are vulnerable to damage from compaction, caused by people, machinery and livestock, if animals are congregating under a tree for any reason. Younger trees are important because they will eventually reach old age and replace the veterans, but any trees which are adversely affecting the veteran trees by shading could be removed; gradually if several are involved.

Many veteran trees were once pollarded, but if this practice ceased some time ago, the decision to repollard is one which requires careful consideration (Figure 4.6). The crowns of such trees can become unstable, requiring some action to be taken. However, restarting pollarding after a long gap can actually accelerate the decline of a veteran tree in some circumstances. Old, neglected pollards may fail if severely cut back, but some species seem to recover well: in one study at Knebworth Park, 93% of old hornbeam pollards that had

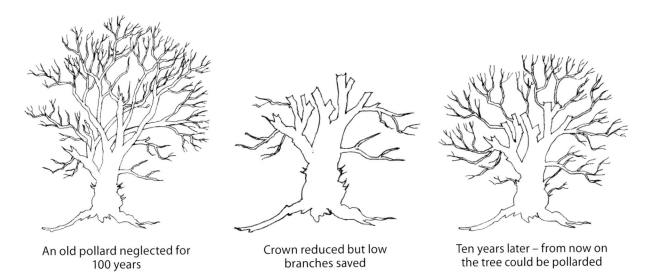

| An old pollard neglected for 100 years | Crown reduced but low branches saved | Ten years later – from now on the tree could be pollarded |

Figure 4.6 Repollarding an old pollard, neglected for 100 years.

not been cut for more than 55 years survived the treatment. Wych elm, willow and lime are also good subjects; variable results have been found with ash, oak and poplar, while veteran beeches often die after severe re-pollarding. More details can be found in *Veteran trees: a guide to good management* (Read, 2000) and *Ancient and other veteran trees: further guidance on management* (Lonsdale, 2013), both of which can be freely downloaded from the Ancient Tree Forum website. The chances of success can be increased by a number of measures, such as leaving branch stubs above the branch collar, choosing rough-barked trees, and leaving some branches intact for 3–5 years until new shoots become established after cutting (Mitchell, 1989). In the case of beech, this appears to be essential and the initial retention of 25–50% of the crown is recommended.

Clues to how a tree might respond to repollarding can be found by carefully examining the growth of the tree, or specimens of the same species, of a similar age nearby. If a tree has been damaged and lost a limb, new shoot growth, active shoot growth from the trunk and a good depth to the canopy are all indications that the tree might respond well to pollarding and pruning. If you are in doubt, a single limb could be removed, and the response of the tree monitored. Good regrowth might indicate that the tree will respond well to being pollarded.

Veteran oaks support rich assemblages of specialist wildlife.

In addition, it is also important to consider the age of the tree, the number of limbs (and hence how much crown) and how the balance of the tree would be affected by pollarding. The number of stages over which the pollarding will be carried out must be decided, what limbs will be left, and the length of snags. Timing is also critical, to avoid periods of bud break and leaf fall in particular: mid to late winter is generally the best time to carry out work on veteran trees. You may also undertake sensitive and gradual thinning around veteran trees to reduce competition from younger trees which might otherwise shade them out.

Managing veteran trees is a specialised undertaking; each tree or population of trees deserves its own management plan; woodland owners are strongly recommended to consult a specialist management guide e.g. Lonsdale (2013) and to seek professional advice. Before any work is carried out, you should consider the affect on the wildlife using the tree. Any work should be undertaken by fully certified chainsaw operators, with certificates for working at heights and for tree climbing.

4.4 **Deadwood**

As we have seen in Section 4.3, deadwood plays a vital role in the life cycle of many woodland organisms, and is therefore a very important component of woodland ecosystems. Many of the inhabitants of deadwood are rare or threatened Priority Species, often with poor dispersal ability. If these include European Protected Species such as the great crested newt, barbastelle and noctule bat, a licence would be required before any management or removal of deadwood is undertaken. Deadwood habitats may be found in a variety of different places in woodland, including:

- living trees of any age, e.g. rot holes and decaying limbs or as dead snags (see also Table 4.3)
- standing dead trees or snags
- stumps
- fallen (windthrown) trees
- accumulations of smaller material such as logs, branches and twigs
- material present below the ground
- deadwood present in rivers and streams.

In the very recent past, people often saw this material as a sign of neglect and were tempted to collect and burn it. Even today, new owners may consider 'tidying' their wood by disposing of the deadwood. However, it is essential to realise that deadwood provides important habitat for small mammals such as bats, voles and hedgehogs, cavity-nesting birds such as willow tit, and a diverse range of insects, lichens, fungi and mosses; and the species that feed on them. Colonisation of deadwood depends on the tree species, the stage of decay, the size and volume of deadwood (colonists have differing micro-habitat requirements) and so on. The fungi which colonise deadwood are absolutely critical, as they predigest wood, allowing other organisms such as insect larvae to move in. Oak deadwood for example decays very slowly, providing long-term continuity; this is particularly apparent in upland oak woods, here there is often a high biomass of fallen branches. In contrast, birch is relatively short-lived, but its rotting hollow stems are good for roosting bats, nesting birds, pine marten and range of insects and fungi. In deciduous woodland, the diversity of species that depend on deadwood is particularly high in wood pasture with pollards, and to some extent in neglected coppice with large, decaying stools. Species diversity is lower in managed coppice and high forest, but storm damage in the late 20th century has increased the deadwood resource.

Some insects such as the wasp beetle whose larvae develop in deadwood or leaf litter, require flowers for the adults to feed on. Flowering plants in nearby woodland rides and glades are therefore critical to the successful lifecycle of these species. For example, the adults of many insects appear to emerge at the time of peak flowering of hawthorn, which appears to be particularly important.

Native pinewoods and old Scottish pine plantations traditionally lost much of their deadwood through management, but pine stumps left *in situ* support rich assemblages, including rare beetles, hoverflies and lichens. Decayed pine snags support nesting crested tit and pin-head lichens; large dead branches may be used by roosting osprey and capercaillie.

In rivers, standing water and wet woodland, deadwood which appears to be polluting or choking can actually be important for healthy freshwater ecosystems. For example, 'debris dams' provide shelter for fish and trap organic matter; wet rotting logs are important for invertebrates (147 species are known to be associated with such material (Humphrey and Bailey, 2012)); and veteran trees by water provide nest holes for birds and burrows for fish.

If your wood has mature native broadleaf trees, and has had little intervention for a long time, the deadwood may have a rich assemblage of species (Table 4.4). Conifer plantations, particularly those over 100 years old, can also contain valuable deadwood resources.

Managing deadwood

There are various opportunities to create or enhance deadwood habitats in most woodland types, irrespective of their past history and management. Many of the key management priorities are generic to a range of deciduous woodland types, and are described below.

- preserve some areas for 'old-growth' conditions
- retain veteran trees
- select and manage suitable trees to take the place of veteran trees in the longer term
- leave dead limbs *in situ* (which requires consideration of health and safety issues)
- leave all deadwood if possible, but some small logs can be lashed together as a pile and placed in dappled shade
- pollarding will increase the value of standing trees for deadwood specialists and provides fallen deadwood
- artificially increasing deadwood in some (especially young and coppice) woods could benefit biodiversity
- set aside some areas of minimal intervention to allow natural build up of deadwood (particularly relevant in some upland woods)
- along some waterways, public access requires consideration of health and safety issues
- non-intervention minimises damage to streamside banks
- allowing dieback of exotic poplars provides nest holes for willow tit.

In Scottish pinewoods and old-growth plantations, the following guidelines also apply:

- lowering management intensity should ensure a supply of deadwood through natural processes
- target $\geq$20–40 m^3 per ha deadwood
- preserve standing dead and dying pines (up to 80 years)
- leave fallen deadwood and stumps
- create some high stumps (1–3 m) for hole-nesting birds.

The UK Forestry Standard (UKFS) guidelines on *Forests and Biodiversity* (Forestry Commission, 2011) – one of a series of seven guidelines concerned with sustainable forest management practices – includes guidance on managing deadwood. Further information can be found in *Managing deadwood in forests and woodlands* (Humphrey and

Wasp beetle larvae feed on dead wood, but adults seek flowers along the woodland edge to feed.

Table 4.4
Strategies for managing deadwood in different woodland types (adapted from Hodge and Peterken, 1998; Humphrey *et al.*, 2002).

Woodland type	Characteristics	Management strategy	Management guidance
Ancient woodland, including coppice and wood pasture supporting rich 'deadwood specialist' fauna and flora	• Mature timber habitat over long time period • History of pollarding • Low intensity management with natural disturbance	• Conserve and enhance veteran trees and deadwood • Allow natural processes to replenish deadwood	• Minimum intervention, small scale thinning to mimic natural processes • Retain veteran trees and trees with decaying wood • Target typically 40–50 m³ per ha deadwood >20 cm • Retain middle-aged trees to form future veteran trees • Consider injuring trees to provide future deadwood • Retain cut wood *in situ* • Leave fallen deadwood *in situ*
Ancient woodland and old secondary woodland with little deadwood and/or 'deadwood specialist' species	• Low deadwood due to management • Lacks large mature deadwood habitat • May lack local source of colonists	• Allow natural processes to expand deadwood • Retain sufficient mature timber to attract colonists and provide future deadwood	• Allow some coppice to develop into high forest if this does not adversely affect other species • Improve structural diversity • Target typically 20–40 m³ per ha deadwood >20 cm • Retain veteran trees and trees with decaying wood • Retain 20–40% of cut wood on site • Leave fallen deadwood *in situ*
PAWS (typically exotic, even-aged stands)	• Deadwood volume from previous stand may be high • Shade from conifers threatens deadwood habitat	• Consider restoration of native woodland whilst protecting deadwood resource	• If undertaking restoration, maintain some semi-shaded conditions to conserve deadwood habitats

Bailey, 2012). Both of these documents are freely available to download from the Forestry Commission website (www.forestry.gov.uk).

Health and safety

There are potential risks associated with any work related to veteran trees and deadwood, for example from falling branches. In all cases, a Site Risk Assessment should be undertaken to identify any hazards posed by individuals, or groups of trees, or before any work is undertaken. Health and safety is also a concern where trees are close to public roads or footpaths. Deadwood issues need to be taken into account, for example where dead limbs are close to recreational areas or footpaths and there is a risk of falling deadwood. In addition to the guides cited above, other guides freely available on the internet include English Nature's *Veteran trees: guide to risk and responsibility* (Davies *et al.*, 2000); the Forestry Commission's *Hazards from trees: a general guide* (Lonsdale, 2000); and *Common sense risk management of trees* (National Tree Safety Group, 2011). You can also visit The Arboricultural Association website (www.trees.org.uk) and if you are concerned about visitor safety to your wood, consult *Managing visitor safety in the countryside* (VSCG, 2011). For any issues related to health and safety, there is no substitute for professional advice.

5 Creating new opportunities for wildlife

5.1 Introducing woodland shade plants

When plant introduction is appropriate
Plant introduction is most appropriate for improving the species diversity of isolated, recent (secondary) woodlands with a sparse field layer, and little prospect of colonisation by shade-tolerant plants. A wide variety of such species can be successfully established in these woods over a period of three to seven years. Small-scale introductions are unlikely to swamp wild populations, especially when they are spatially remote from ancient woods, and local collections can maximise genetic diversity. But if overdone, there is a danger that introductions could obscure natural biogeographical boundaries, so that recent woods may begin to resemble ancient woods, which would not be good conservation practice.

When not to introduce plants
For nature conservation reasons, introducing herbaceous plants into the woodland field layer of ancient woodland, including PAWS, should generally not be undertaken. In the past, species such as wild daffodil and bluebell have been planted to make woods look 'more attractive', or in the belief that woodland biodiversity can be increased by planting species which would otherwise be unlikely or very slow to colonise. This assumes that the species introduced would naturally occur in that particular area or habitat. However, such planting risks bringing non-local ecotypes into the local landscape which could be detrimental to other components of the woodland ecosystem. Introduced plants may also have a narrow genetic base resulting from their artificial selection in a nursery and, in some cases, non-native species can be accidentally introduced, that are more vigorous and subsequently hybridise with native species. Spanish bluebell is an example of a species that may now be present in up to 15% of Britain's woodlands. If Spanish or hybrid bluebells are present in your wood, they should be removed to prevent them spreading further into the countryside; for identification and further information see *Bluebells for Britain* (Plantlife, 2003).

Existing semi-natural herbaceous plant communities in ancient woodland should not be artificially modified through indiscriminate planting for aesthetic purposes. There may be a better argument for reintroducing species which have been lost, but even this must be carried out very carefully. Planting into recent woodlands in close proximity to ancient woods is also to be discouraged, to avoid risks to the genetic integrity of the ancient woodland flora. In any case, woodland so positioned has a better chance of natural colonisation by the desired species, although the rate is likely to be very slow for most ancient woodland species. However, there are exceptions, and some ancient woodland species may colonise the margins of recent woodland (Table 5.1), but even these species must compete with faster colonising shade-tolerant plants such as common nettle and bramble.

Table 5.1
Examples of ancient woodland plants capable of dispersal from lowland ancient woodland into the adjacent recent woodland.

Black bryony	Enchanter's-nightshade	Remote sedge
Bluebell	Moschatel	Three-nerved sandwort
Common spotted-orchid	Pendulous sedge	Wood speedwell
Dog's mercury	Pignut	Yellow archangel

Selecting and sourcing plants

If the introduction of herbaceous plants into the woodland field layer is deemed appropriate, there are several options for obtaining seed or plants. Carefully select a mix of species based on site conditions in your wood with reference to the ground flora present in local woodland – so called 'reference sites' (refer to surveys described in Section 2.4). A range of woodland herbs, grasses and sedges should be specified, although species with limited distributions would not normally be included. The cost per species from a commercial wildflower seed company will be higher than if you purchase their standard woodland mixes, but may be less expensive if fewer species are specified. A useful reference to support species selection is the Highways Agency's *The establishment of an herbaceous plant layer in roadside woodland* (Highway's Agency, 2005) available on their website, which includes lists of native herbs and grasses appropriate to the Forestry Commission's seed zones throughout the British Isles, together with their preferred soil types and conditions.

Commercial seed companies also offer 'generic' woodland and hedgerow mixes which typically contain 15–20 wild flowers alone, or mixed with grasses. However, the wild flower component often includes species chosen for their colour and reliable germination, and may not have been collected locally (Table 5.2). Some grow well both in light and shade on moderately fertile soils, but others are less tolerant of shade. Only a small proportion of ancient woodland plants are usually included in a mix. Wild flowers are likely to do less well when mixed with grasses which compete for the same resources, particularly in mixes containing a high percentage by weight of turf grasses such as common bent and smooth meadow-grass. Herb mixes alone, or supplemented with a low density of local woodland grasses such as wood meadow-grass are more likely to succeed.

A more expensive option is to plant small patches with cell-grown plants, particularly those species which are difficult to propagate by seed. The range of plants available commercially is more limited, but includes species such as primrose, bluebell, violets, woodruff and yellow archangel. Again, the provenance of plug plants purchased from commercial companies may not be local.

To overcome some of these concerns, you might consider collecting your own seed from local ancient woods on similar soil types, in which case local provenance would be more assured. Collections also offer the chance to maximise genetic diversity and reduce the risks to co-evolved species such as insect feeders and pollinators. It is important though to avoid over-harvesting; plants should not be dug up, and there is still the risk of imposing artificial selection pressures in small collections. The landowner's permission will be required and collecting seed can be time-consuming. Many species seed early in woodlands: some will need to be collected from May onwards and stored in a dry, cool place. If you

Table 5.2
Herbs which are typically found in commercial mixes of woodland plants.

Ancient woodland plants	Faster colonising woodland herbs	Shade-tolerant herbs
Bluebell	Foxglove	Agrimony
Nettle-leaved bellflower	Garlic mustard	Betony
Pignut	Greater stitchwort	Cowslip
Primrose	Hedge woundwort	Hedge bedstraw
Ramsons	Red campion	Meadowsweet
	Upright hedge-parsley	Perforate St John's-wort
	Wood avens	Ragged-robin
	Wood sage	Selfheal
		Tufted vetch
		Yarrow

miss the critical time, the seed may already have been shed – ramsons, for example, loses most of its seed within a week when ripe. The sowing conditions are important and a good seedbed is essential for effective germination and establishment. Suitable preparation can be provided by light surface cultivation or, if much vegetation is present (in rides for example), it can be pre-treated with herbicide and the seed sown directly into the killed sward. Alternatively, if the vegetation is sparse, the seed can be broadcast and covered with a thin surface mulch of leaf litter or other suitable material. Sowing into a continuous cover of vegetation without any ground preparation will achieve nothing.

Introduction methods

Introducing herbaceous plants into large areas of woodland would be prohibitively expensive and unnecessary. Sowing or planting in discrete patches should both enhance the diversity of the woodland field layer whilst allowing plants to colonise other parts of the wood. A number of factors to consider when determining the suitability of the site are listed in Table 5.3. Most of these parameters need to be met if the introduction of plants is to be successful, with appropriate light levels and lack of weed competition being especially important; so planting in open areas or under the deep shade of conifer plantations for example will not be successful.

Plants of the woodland interior such as bluebell, primrose and ramsons are likely to establish best in shady areas where there is little competition, but even these species will struggle if light levels are too low. The fast-germinating woodland edge herbs included in commercial woodland mixes would do better in areas with more variation in sunlight, such as the shrubby margins of rides and glades. More rapid growth and flowering is likely to occur in this environment, but competition from bramble, ivy, bracken or grasses such as cock's-foot may be more of a problem.

In established woodland where the ground vegetation is sparse, there should be no need for any special ground preparation. Sow the seed in the autumn (September–November), avoiding waterlogged soils, or early spring before the frosts finish (February–April) to provide the chilling required by many woodland species. Sowing rates depend upon which species are being sown, but rates of 1 g per m^2 for grass/herb mixes and 0.5 g per m^2 for herbs alone should suffice. If a standard woodland mix is used, the fast-germinating herbs

Table 5.3
Site suitability for introducing field layer herbaceous woodland plants (after Highways Agency, 2005).

Site parameters	Preferred state
Overall quality	Good structural diversity in canopy, understorey and leaf litter, leading to varied light conditions.
Light level	Shady to control competitive light-demanding weeds; 15–40% daylight at ground level
Canopy composition	Mixed canopy of native broadleaves and/or native Scots pine, avoiding dense single species plantations
Existing ground vegetation	<30% existing ground vegetation
Dominant weeds	<10% bramble, ivy or bracken; no grassy sward
Soil characteristics	Humid and moist, avoiding winter waterlogged or compacted areas
Aspect and slope	North, east or possibly west-facing slopes, and those less than 1:1.5 are less likely to dry out
Leaf litter	At least 30% cover of leaf litter on soil surface to provide good germination conditions
Patch size	Minimum area 5 x 40 m (0.02 ha)
Location of wood	>1 km from ancient woodland

Introducing cell-grown wild flowers into 'light' shade of a young, recent woodland can be a family occasion.

will initially dominate, with interior woodland species not becoming prominent for three years or so. This may not be a problem if you design a woodland interior mix, rather than accepting a proprietary mix.

The more light-demanding species planted along the woodland edge will also benefit from periodic management of the scrubby edge by coppicing and thinning (see Sections 3.3 and 4.1), providing this does not result in too much competition from invasive weeds. If bramble, ivy, bracken, common nettle, thistles or sward grasses become a problem, their spread can be controlled (see Section 4.1), remembering that these species are also valuable components of the woodland flora.

For cell-grown plants, Francis *et al.* (1992) found that 6–9 plants per m^2 gave good results, with species such as bluebell, primrose and wood sage, and that this could be reduced to 3–4 plants per m^2 for species with good vegetative spread such as bugle and yellow archangel. Cell-grown plants are best planted out in spring whilst the soil is still moist, in small groups, possibly in combination with sown plants.

5.2 Bird nestboxes

Bird nestboxes can make an enormous difference to the populations of some species, but in many woods they are simply not necessary. First of all you need to assess the availability of natural nest holes in your wood. Mature woodland which has good structural diversity and trees of a wide age range, including older trees with holes and cavities and similar nest sites, is unlikely to benefit from nestboxes. This conclusion may be confirmed if you find evidence of the presence of good populations of a range of hole-nesting birds: consider carrying out a woodland bird survey in spring (see Section 2.3). If there are already enough nesting places, boxes can actually upset the balance of species if they encourage the populations of commoner birds such as blue tit, which can compete aggressively with much rarer species such as marsh tit for nest sites and food (Symes and Currie, 2005). Nestboxes might be considered if a particular species such as pied flycatcher or willow tit is declining or absent, in which case boxes could be put up specifically for the target species, especially if suitable nest holes are in limited supply.

Similar issues arise if you have a new woodland at the stage of canopy closure. Here there will be few if any natural hole-nesting opportunities, but putting up nestboxes will attract relatively common species such as blue tit and great tit. These birds normally feed in the higher canopy, but in young woodland, they might compete for food with declining understorey specialists such as nightingale, garden warbler and willow warbler.

In contrast, nestboxes may be much more successful in secondary lowland woodland with poor structural diversity, lacking older trees, and hence with few opportunities for hole-nesting birds. Mature woods that have been heavily managed, with few old trees remaining, also lack natural tree holes; examples include lowland mixed deciduous woodland converted to conifer plantations or chestnut coppice with few oak standards remaining; and many of the heavily managed upland oak woods in western Britain. Pied flycatcher and common redstart in particular, which have declined in western oak woods, have benefitted enormously from major nestbox schemes, providing the woodland has sufficient food resources available.

Nestboxes can also be successfully employed for owls in young woodland, or larger open areas associated with mature woodland or plantations. Barn owl boxes erected 3–5 m above the ground on a solitary mature tree or pole may also attract other species such as kestrel and stock dove.

Nestbox design

There is a wealth of literature published by conservation organisations such as the RSPB which describes the construction and siting of nestboxes, and you may derive considerable pleasure from constructing your own boxes. A useful guide to nestbox design is *The BTO Nestbox Guide* (Du Feu, 2004; 2005). However, self-built nestboxes, whilst relatively cheap to construct, tend to suffer from poor durability and may need to be replaced every few years. An alternative material is woodcrete, a mix of wood, clay and concrete, which is available commercially. These boxes are far more durable, secure from predators and provide a better internal environment for young birds, but are more expensive than timber boxes.

You can purchase nestboxes as standard designs for commoner species, and specific designs for those with more specialist requirements. Standard designs have 10 cm high open fronts for species such as robin and pied wagtail, or 6 cm for spotted flycatcher; closed fronts with small holes (25 mm diameter) are suitable for blue tit and coal tit; and slightly larger holes (28 mm) for great tit and pied flycatcher. Large boxes with larger holes support little owl, great spotted woodpecker and starling. All should mimic natural nesting sites.

You need to place nestboxes at a safe distance above the ground to protect the birds from predators such as domestic cats. Nestboxes for tits for example should be 2–4 m up a tree, in a shaded place, or facing north east. Open-fronted nestboxes for robins or wrens should be less than 2 m above the ground, so they need to be well hidden in dense vegetation. In contrast, open-fronted nestboxes for spotted flycatcher should be 2–4 m above ground, preferably sheltered by vegetation such as ivy. Some additional protection can be provided against predators such as squirrels and great spotted woodpeckers by placing a metal plate around the entrance hole to prevent its widening.

5.3 Nestboxes and roosting boxes for mammals

Bat boxes

Bats roost both individually and in small groups, and may use many roost sites over the course of a year. In woodland, bats naturally roost in any species of tree with suitable holes, crevices and so on, which provide them with shelter and protection from predators. These sites are often close to feeding areas. Small cracks and crevices may support individual bats, but larger holes are required for maternity roosts. Bats also roost in tangled climbers such as ivy and honeysuckle, which is a good reason for protecting climbers in your wood. In many parts of Britain, the loss of old-growth woodland has significantly reduced the roosting opportunities for bats. Bat boxes may be able to help to some extent by providing artificial roost sites, particularly in recent woodland and plantations on ancient woodland sites.

If you are considering putting up bat boxes, the first thing to do is to survey your wood following the guidelines described in Section 2.4, to establish what the need might be. If your wood is part of a larger woodland complex, the survey should encompass the woodland as a whole to establish what opportunities there are for bats to roost in the immediate vicinity. If there are plenty of small cracks and crevices in the trees, but a lack of larger holes, then bat boxes could provide opportunities for summer maternity roosts.

Some bat boxes are designed to be used throughout the year, but if they are constructed from normal thicknesses of wood, the bats may be forced to leave during the winter in extremely cold weather. In reality, the majority of bat boxes currently in place are most likely to be used from April to November. At higher altitudes, occupancy might be expected between late May and September. These are generally known as 'summer' boxes. They may be purchased from a number of suppliers or constructed following instructions provided by the Bat Conservation Trust and local bat groups on their respective websites. Designs may differ, but there are some important generic issues relating to their use. Boxes should be large enough for bats in maternity roosts to cluster to conserve heat, so their internal dimensions should be at least 10 x 10 x 10 cm. Whilst the depth is most important because many species like confined spaces, the width may be increased to 15 cm and the height to 30 cm. Boxes have traditionally been made out of rough-sawn timber so that bats can land to investigate the boxes, cling and climb. Wood preservatives are harmful to bats and should not be used. It is also important that boxes have well-sealed joints giving good insulation and no draughts, to ensure that the internal temperature and humidity remains constant. The entrance is usually a slit at the base, typically 1.5–1.8 cm wide and 4 cm long; anything wider would allow birds to nest in the box. Such boxes may last no more than 10 years. An alternative are the Schwegler woodcrete boxes, which are more expensive to purchase, but are more durable, and have good thermal insulation with less fluctuation of internal temperatures.

Winter boxes specifically designed for hibernation are also being developed, based on the dimensions of natural tree holes used by bats, but these have not yet been widely used (Stebbings and Walsh, 1991). These boxes need to be insulated against extreme cold, so must be constructed with walls 10 cm thick, or possibly from a hollowed out log. Schwegler woodcrete winter boxes are also available.

Location

Boxes may be attached to trees in woodland, usually at least 5 m high, which reduces the risk of vandalism, but will require ladders to put them up and inspect them. Consequently, health and safety must be taken into consideration and a risk assessment carried out before these tasks are undertaken. You should firmly attach bat boxes to a tree in a sheltered position with the boxes having good exposure to the sun, for example along the woodland perimeter, or the edge of woodland rides and glades. Boxes in these locations should also be easier to find and inspect on subsequent visits. Avoid obstructions close to the box and remove any leafy branches overhanging the box. Boxes are more likely to be occupied if there is prime feeding habitat nearby, such as a shrubby woodland edge or wetland. It may help to put the

**Schwegler woodcrete bat box with
open-bottomed slot.**

Woodland owners putting up bat boxes.

boxes up on a sunny day, so that good positions can be found. Bats should also be given the opportunity to choose between boxes facing a variety of aspects, south being the warmest, with others being cooler, depending on shading. Boxes on a single tree may be positioned facing south, south east and south west for example.

Boxes can only be inspected by someone with an appropriate licence; as it is an offence under the Wildlife and Countryside Act 1981 (as amended) to disturb bats. Boxes should not be inspected from the beginning of June to the middle of August as heavily pregnant, or lactating bats with a baby/pup may be present. Frequent inspections, perhaps every six to eight weeks are not usually a problem, but once bats are discovered it is unwise to inspect it again that summer (unless there is a scientific purpose to do so). Boxes that remain unused after several years can be removed and re-positioned elsewhere, but those that have been used should be left in place. Bat droppings are the best indicator that bats have visited a box; these tend to be black or brown and quite variable in size and shape. However, they lack the white areas usually seen in bird droppings and crumble to a fine dust when rubbed between thumb and forefinger.

Finally, it is important to remember that bat boxes are a serious commitment in terms of inspection and cleaning, particularly if they have sealed bottoms. Even if you can persuade local bat groups to help with the initiation of a bat box project, there is no guarantee that volunteers will be able to maintain the boxes over a long period of time, which is essential if they are to remain habitable. One alternative would be to use open-bottomed slot boxes as these do not require cleaning and maintenance.

Dormouse boxes

Boxes have also been designed for small terrestrial mammals such as dormouse, red squirrel and hedgehog. Dormice favour extensive areas of ancient woodland with hazel coppice and a diverse range of shrubs; they also use a range of scrub types, hedgerows and young plantations. The dormouse is nocturnal and feeds mainly in the branches of trees and shrubs. It prefers to nest in tree holes, old bird nests and squirrel dreys, but will also construct a nest in tangled scrubby vegetation such as bramble.

Dormouse nestboxes have been widely used for survey and monitoring programmes, but they can provide valuable breeding sites when natural holes are in short supply. Nestboxes

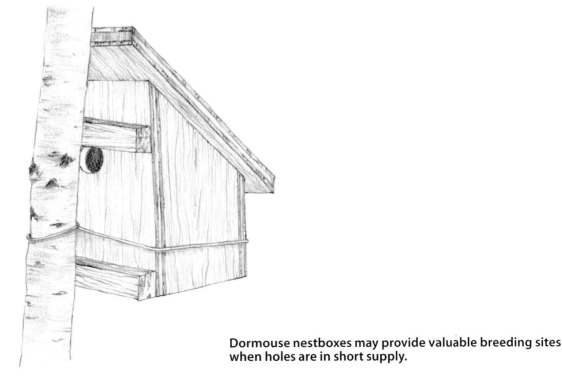

Dormouse nestboxes may provide valuable breeding sites when holes are in short supply.

are readily occupied by dormice, thus boosting local populations. They are also very useful in young woodland or habitat which has been disturbed, providing opportunities for population growth. Plastic nest tubes are also used to survey dormouse populations, but cannot substitute for nest boxes where conservation is the main aim.

For hibernation, dormouse boxes are not used as the internal temperature within a nestbox is too variable. Dormice require cool temperatures and damp conditions for hibernation, and construct a tightly woven nest on or under the ground, typically in hollow tree stumps and at the base of coppice stools.

If you are considering putting up dormouse nestboxes, first investigate the natural nesting opportunities for dormice in your wood. If the wood is part a larger woodland complex, then consider the woodland as a whole to establish whether there are good nest sites close by. It is also worth establishing if dormice are breeding, or visiting the wood, following the guidelines set out in Section 2.4.

Dormice nestboxes are similar in appearance to bird boxes, the main difference being the positioning of the entrance hole at the back, facing the tree. Boxes should be placed about 2.5 m above the ground, ideally near a routeway which dormice might be using. Dormice are easily disturbed by approaching people, so public areas should be avoided. Nestboxes are relatively easily to construct, or they may be purchased from specialist suppliers. Like bats, dormice are a protected species, so should not be disturbed, unless a special licence has been obtained from Natural England.

Red squirrel nestboxes

In some parts of Britain where you are lucky enough to have red squirrels present in your wood, or in woodland close by, you may have considered putting up nestboxes for them. Most woodland is likely to have sufficient nest sites for red squirrels, so the animals may only use a box occasionally, usually in summer and autumn. Nestboxes can provide refuges in bad weather, if dreys are dislodged by high winds for example, and dispersing youngsters may seek refuge in boxes. For these reasons, woodland owners should not be disappointed if nestboxes remain unused.

Nestboxes are normally placed about 4 m above the ground, although squirrel dreys may be found much higher in the canopy. They are available commercially, and designs for their construction can be found on the 'Save our Squirrels' website (www.saveoursquirrels.org.uk/). Once in place, nestboxes should not be disturbed if they are being used. The red squirrel is listed on Appendix III of the Bern Convention and is protected by Schedules 5 and 6 of the Wildlife and Countryside Act; a special licence is required to disturb these animals. In any case, if you have red squirrels in your wood, it is now an offence to intentionally or recklessly:

- kill, injure or take (capture) a red squirrel
- damage, destroy or obstruct access to any structure or place which a red squirrel uses for shelter or protection
- disturb a red squirrel while it is occupying a structure or place which it uses for that purpose.

Detailed guidance on surveys and management operations to minimise disturbance to red squirrels may be found in *Forest operations and red squirrels* (Forestry Commission Scotland, 2006a); *Managing forests as red squirrel strongholds* (Forestry Commission Scotland, 2012); and *Practical techniques for surveying and monitoring squirrels* (Gurnell *et al.*, 2009).

One important consideration when contemplating nestboxes for red squirrels is the presence of grey squirrels in your wood. In areas where both species are present, such as the Borders, parts of Northern England and mainland Wales, nestboxes put up for red squirrels may be used by both species, which may not be desirable. Grey squirrels carry squirrelpox virus, which they appear to be immune to, but is normally fatal for red squirrels. Although it is not known how the virus is passed from grey squirrels to red squirrels, it is possible that this could occur if red squirrels use feeders visited by grey squirrels infected with the virus (Fiegna *et al.*, 2015). Where both species occur, boxes can be used as part of a control programme for grey squirrel; for further details on squirrel control, refer to *Controlling grey squirrel damage to woodlands* (Mayle *et al.*, 2007).

5.4 Woodland ponds

Ponds frequently provide excellent wildlife habitat and collectively support a significant proportion of British wetland flora and fauna. Some insects, amphibians and plants are only found in ponds, highlighting their importance in the conservation of freshwater biodiversity in Britain. Ponds are common in woodlands in many parts of Britain, and include old hammer ponds and mill ponds, natural shallow flashes and shallow pools along trackways. Natural ponds often occur in close proximity to other wetland habitat such as streams, seepages in wet woods and other ponds. Woodland ponds are usually shaded, often heavily. They may support rare and specialised communities. They are particularly good for dragonflies, and may contain important assemblages of species of conservation concern such as Nationally Scarce water beetles and great crested newt (a European Protected Species).

Although ponds are widespread in Britain, examples supporting healthy populations of wildlife are becoming increasingly rare. Consequently, ponds are now included on the list of Priority Habitats, and may be classified as a priority pond if they meet one or more criteria:

- they are habitats of international importance
- they contain species of high conservation importance
- they support exceptional populations or numbers of key species
- they are of high ecological quality.

To identify whether a woodland pond represents a priority habitat will require a survey to examine factors such as vegetation types or specific species groups.

Pond restoration and management

If you have a pond in your woodland, advice may be sought from the Freshwater Habitats Trust, or your local wildlife trust to help you determine its quality and whether there are priority species which would benefit from any kind of restoration. An overgrown pond may appear to be in need of management, but many woodland ponds have a lot of plants in them, with relatively little open water; they may contain fallen branches and other deadwood which is excellent habitat for aquatic wildlife and should not be removed unless it constitutes a risk to health and safety. Insects also benefit from decaying leaf litter on the pond floor, submerged tree roots and the muddy edges of shady ponds. Consequently, a pond survey should be undertaken before any management is carried out. The survey should place particular emphasis on assessing: aquatic, marginal and semi-terrestrial animals such as ground beetles; and shade-loving plants such as mosses and liverworts. Invasive habitat management involving the removal of plants or dredging should only be considered if the wildlife in the pond will not be put at risk.

Trees also contribute significantly to the biodiversity of a woodland pond, and in many circumstances are best left alone. This includes mature woodland over 50 years old with long-established ponds, and wet woodland where alders and willows grow close to, or within a pond. Practical management in these circumstances should be resisted, particularly the removal of: large amounts of leaf litter; branches and fallen trees; mature trees that provide shade to the pond; and substantial areas of willows growing within a pond (source Freshwater Habitats Trust). If any 'restoration' work is undertaken, the effects should be carefully monitored before further management is undertaken.

There may be some circumstances where woodland ponds might benefit from some management, for example if the surrounding trees have grown up in the past 30 years or so, in an area that was formerly more open. Trees may be cut back or removed to allow more light to reach a pond, but it can be difficult to predict whether this will be beneficial or harmful to the aquatic ecosystem. Reducing shading can encourage a greater diversity of plants and animals, but too much light may favour unwanted plant species such as duckweed and bulrush, which could dominate the pond and ultimately cause serious damage to the aquatic community. Rare or uncommon species present before the management commenced might even be lost. To avoid such an outcome, it would be wise to reduce the shade by no more than 25%, gradually over a five year period, monitoring the effects on the pond community very carefully. Woodland owners should also be mindful of the fact that trees and scrub away from the immediate pond edge may act as a 'buffer zone', providing some protection to the pond and its environs and allowing the safe movement of amphibians and small mammals from the pond into the surrounding landscape. A very useful guide that should be consulted before starting any management operations is the Freshwater Habitats Trust leaflet on *Managing trees around ponds*, freely available on their website (www.freshwaterhabitats.org.uk); the Trust have also published a guide to pond management that includes those found in woodlands, *The Pond Book: a guide to the management and creation of ponds* (Williams *et al.*, 2010).

Creation of new ponds

Pond creation in woodland can be particularly valuable in today's intensively managed landscapes, as there are few opportunities for ponds to form naturally. However, you should avoid the temptation of managing or 'restoring' an existing pond. New ponds with clean water can make an important contribution to the conservation of freshwater wildlife by

The broad-bodied chaser is likely to be one of the first dragonflies to colonise a new woodland pond.

acting as stepping stones to improve ecological connectivity, increasing the diversity of ponds in an area, and strengthening local populations of Priority Species such as the common toad and the three-lobed water-crowfoot. For this reason it is useful to have some knowledge of wetland habitat in the area, and how a new pond might add value.

Ponds are probably best created in recent woodlands where there is no risk of damaging ancient woodland habitat. In any case, it is important to ensure that the site for pond creation is not selected because it is already 'damp', as such an area might be a natural spring or a seasonal flush which constitutes important habitat in its own right, which should be protected. Locate a pond near to wet areas, but not in them. If your subsoil includes clay there is a good chance that the pond will hold water; sandy and chalky soils do not support ponds unless they have plastic pond liners. It is also important that a new pond does not alter local hydrology, risking damage to nearby protected habitat; or adversely impact on drainage or water courses. It should not be at risk from pollution, or require planning permission. Pre-site checks in a woodland setting might include:

- potential impact on protected species or designated sites
- potential impact on archaeology
- need for trees to be felled or coppiced
- impact on hydrology
- health and safety.

There are many different designs and features which you may consider at the planning stage for a woodland pond. The Freshwater Habitats Trust habitat factsheet on *Designing wildlife ponds in woodland* (one of a series on pond location, design, planning, construction and management included in the Pond Creation Toolkit) includes the following advice:

- Hydrology – ensure the pond will hold water for at least some of the year.
- Size – a pond with a diameter of about 30 m should allow light to reach the water surface on the northern side of the pond, whilst the southern edge will remain shaded if the pond is surrounded by trees.
- Location and leaf litter – leaves of alder and willows degrade better in water than those of trees such as oak and ash, so consider the surrounding tree species and their likely contribution to pond sediments.
- Depth – shallow edges will favour marginal plants, and disturbance from animals coming to drink will also be beneficial.
- Islands – if the pond is large enough, small islands will add to the biodiversity value but must be low to avoid tree regeneration.
- Base – as wooded ponds tend to fill in more quickly from leaf litter, an undulating base can extend the life of the pond, and provide bare areas on top of submerged bars.

Designs and drawings are essential for those involved in pond creation, including contractors and if required, planning officers. Project costs should also be carefully worked out before work commences. The construction phase will require careful planning, including timing for dry conditions, and access for machinery to deal with topsoil and spoil. You may wish to undertake this with the help of family and friends, or with a contractor. For more detailed information, download the Freshwater Habitats Trust woodland factsheet.

Finally, if you create a new pond, you may be tempted to visit nearby ponds to collect plants, and possibly beetles and other aquatic animals to give nature a 'helping hand'. This is unnecessary, and should not be undertaken. In contrast to many terrestrial communities, such as plants of the woodland floor, ponds are colonised very quickly, by a wide range of plants and insects. Some of these will be specialists of ponds with bare surfaces, so it is important to allow these plants and animals an opportunity to use the new pond in the early years, before it takes on the character of a more mature pond.

6 Woodlands in a changing climate

6.1 Climate change and woodland communities

Climate change is now indisputable and it is widely accepted that as a result of past emissions of greenhouse gases such as carbon dioxide and methane, the earth will continue to warm during the 21st century. This may have profound consequences for global ecosystems and people's lives. The rate and magnitude of warming will depend on future emissions and concentrations of greenhouse gases, which is dependent on the actions of governments across the world over the next few years on curbing emissions. Climate change in Britain has been projected to the end of the century, based on different greenhouse gas emission scenarios (http://ukclimateprojections.metoffice.gov.uk/). It is expected that summers in Britain will get warmer, and winters milder, with fewer days of frost in many areas. Winters are also projected to be wetter over the majority of Britain, with lower rainfall in the summer in some areas. The sea level around Britain is likely to continue to rise. Climate change is also expected to cause changes to the seasons, affect wind speeds and increase the frequency of extreme weather events such as storms. For more detailed information on projected climate change in Britain, the Living With Environmental Change Network has produced a very helpful Report Card (Morecroft and Speakman, 2015). The UK Climate Projections (UKCP09) website, based on methodology designed by the Met Office, provides maps and graphs on a national and regional basis, illustrating projected climate change to the end century, based on different CO_2 emissions scenarios. Despite a wealth of information, the future is still uncertain, as the projections are just that – uncertain signposts towards future options for adapting to climate change. But climate change cannot be ignored, and the precautionary principle demands that woodland owners and managers think carefully about how to respond. There is very good evidence to suggest that climate change is already affecting wildlife in Britain and these impacts are likely to increase in the future. Examples of how these changes are being manifested include species expanding their range (generally further north), altitudinal shifts (to higher altitudes) colonisation by non-native species, species populations response to extreme events and changes in community phenology (the timing of natural events).

Woodland communities

Woodland communities are already being affected by climate change, which is clearly illustrated by the timing of bud break in spring. For example, some woodland trees and shrubs are already flushing much earlier in southern England than they were 20 or 30 years ago (Collinson and Sparks, 2008; Smithers and Sparks, 2010; Sparks and Crick, 2015). This trend could change the balance of tree communities; for example oaks could begin to dominate at the expense of ash in southern oak-ash woodlands.

Scientists have developed sophisticated models to study the effects of projected climate change on the composition of woodland communities and the distribution of selected species. Forestry Commission studies using the Ecological Site Classification decision support system indicate that climate change will affect woodland succession and species assemblages, leading to gradual but widespread changes in woodland communities. The Environmental Change Institute at the University of Oxford leads the way in this kind of research (Walmsley et al., 2007), though even their results cannot forecast with any precision the actual effect on the ground. Nevertheless, the insights that the models provide give some indication of how woodlands might change over the coming decades. For example, beech might be expected to expand in the north and west, but within its natural range in southern Britain it may be vulnerable and lose its potential as a timber tree, particularly on thin soils on south-facing slopes.

Concern has been expressed over lowland beech and yew woodland; although beech is projected to thrive in projected climate change scenarios, its vulnerability to drought may affect its competitive ability with oak for example (Carey, 2015). Although Carey suggests that major changes in the canopy of lowland mixed deciduous woodland is unlikely over the coming decades, climate modelling indicates that there may be increases in large- and small-leaved limes, where these species occur, at the expense of oak, ash, sycamore and occasionally hornbeam (Berry *et al.*, 2012). In contrast, upland oakwoods and upland ashwoods are thought to be the least vulnerable woodland habitats to climate change, although in oakwoods species such as hornbeam could become a competitor to the dominant sessile oak, together with beech and sycamore. Some ground flora species in upland oakwoods such as wood sorrel and male fern may lose climate space.

Early flowering woodland plants such as wood anemone could suffer from shading if different phenological responses develop between canopy species and plants in the ground flora. Disruptions to the synchrony of woodland events may cause some mismatches in plant-pollinator relationships to develop in the future; it is also likely that mismatches will occur between the breeding of migrant birds and the abundance of prey, although there is limited evidence on how widespread such effects might be (Morrison and Robinson, 2015). Inevitably it seems that the composition of woodland communities will change. Of particular concern to woodland owners, storms are projected to increase in frequency, which could cause longer term damage and bring about changes in woodland ecosystems. The death of tree species such as beech, birch and sycamore could result from drought (Sparks and Crick, 2015) and could also lead to changes in woodland ecosystems, particularly in the south. There will of course be beneficiaries, and in these cases it could be species which require deadwood. Other beneficiaries of climate change might be exotic pests such as the oak processionary moth that was accidentally introduced into Britain in 2005; there have been several outbreaks in the South East in recent years (Hoppit, 2014). Other pests and diseases (native and exotic) also represent a significant threat to woodland tree species, as the spread of ash dieback clearly demonstrates (see Section 3.7).

6.2 Sourcing seed in a changing climate

When seed of trees or shrubs is required for enrichment planting or the creation of new woodland, it has been widely assumed that 'local' seed is best. In this context, the term 'local' usually refers to the source of the plant material, i.e. the location from which the seed was collected. 'Local provenance' is another term sometimes used to describe seed collected locally, but strictly it should only be applied to populations of trees known to be adapted to local conditions, and not to have been introduced by humans. In contrast, the 'origin' of seed is the natural range from which a species was originally derived.

The Forestry Commission's Voluntary Scheme for the Certification of Native Trees and Shrubs aimed to match native seed sources to planting sites, particularly for semi-natural and new native woodlands (Herbert *et al.*, 1999; Forestry Commission Scotland, 2006b). Twenty-four local seed zones were designated, based on major climatic, geological and landform divisions in Britain, each divided into two altitude bands, above or below 300 m. Natural distributions of native trees and shrubs within these zones were taken into consideration and a special set of collection zones drawn up for indigenous Scots pine. With this exception, the main seed zones are probably rather conservative because relatively little is known about genetic diversity in British trees, or how their populations will respond to environmental changes as the climate warms. Consequently the Forestry Commission have published updated guidelines on sourcing seed for adaptation to climate change, based on a portfolio approach (www.forestry.gov.uk).

In practice, the gaps in our knowledge of tree genetics mean that we should continue to include some seed of local and regional provenance for enrichment planting and woodland

Fruits of spindle ready for collection in November.

creation, following the Forestry Commission native seed zones. The Forestry Commission recommends that at least one third of planting stock on any given site should be of local or regional provenance, supplemented by material from at least one source from marginally more southerly provenances (Forestry Commission England, 2010). Eastern European sources should be avoided (Hubert and Cundall, 2006). With any source, seed should be collected from sufficient trees in semi-natural stands to capture as much genetic diversity as possible, to give planted trees the best chance to adapt to climate change (Blakesley and Buckley, 2010). The following guidelines should help if you are planning to collect seed locally:

- Collect seed from healthy, viable tree populations in semi-natural stands such as ancient woodland; avoid woods which are close to other stands or plantations where the trees have been selected in breeding programmes for forestry purposes.
- Conditions at the collection site should match as closely as possible the characteristics of the planting site in terms of the local climate, topography, soil and vegetation type.
- Collect from a reasonable number of individuals, say 20–30, as widely spaced as possible (at least 50–100 m apart) to avoid closely related trees.

Further details on seed collection may be found in the Forestry Commission's *Using local stock for planting native trees and shrubs* (Herbert *et al.*, 1999) and the Royal Botanic Gardens Kew's *UK National Tree Seed Project Seed Collecting Manual* (Kallow, 2014).

6.3 **Connectivity and habitat networks**

In the past, conservation has focused heavily on protecting individual sites such as ancient woodland and species-rich grassland. Many sites are relatively small, and in some areas, they are highly fragmented. To cope with climate change, natural ecosystems will need to respond and adapt quickly, and species may need to move through the landscape. Limited reserves therefore can no longer guarantee long term protection, and the wider countryside will need to play a much greater role in supporting wildlife. Furthermore, large areas of habitat may be necessary to enable some species to survive extreme weather events such as drought (Oliver *et al.*, 2015). Conservationists must consider how existing areas of semi-natural habitat and the wider countryside can best be managed in an integrated way to support the dispersal and colonisation of species which is likely to take place.

Management plans for semi-natural habitats may need to be reviewed and modified, but a much greater problem will be to overcome the large areas of inhospitable countryside that currently surrounds many of our protected areas and sites of conservation interest. The concept of ecological networks is one which has received a great deal of attention in recent years, which combines habitat creation and restoration in the wider landscape with the conservation of existing biodiversity by maintaining and expanding protected areas. This was emphasised in the report *Making Space for Nature* (Lawton *et al.*, 2010), which identified the need for 'large-scale habitat restoration and recreation, under-pinned by the re-establishment of ecological processes and ecosystem services, for the benefits of both people and wildlife'. The report called for the creation of ecological networks, through habitat creation and restoration, and the expansion of existing protected areas. These actions are probably the most important ways of minimising the effects of climate change on semi-natural habitats and wildlife in Britain (e.g. Hopkins, 2007; The Wildlife Trusts, 2007). Public perceptions of ecological networks have received little consideration in the development of this concept, and it has been argued that the cultural services provided to communities by landscape and ecological networks deserve more attention (Ingwood *et al.*, 2015).

Connectivity might be restored between isolated patches of core woodland by creating new woodland or hedgerows, which act as buffers or dispersal routes, thus establishing a woodland habitat network. This would enable the more 'mobile' species to move between patches of woodland as they may naturally have done prior to human disturbance of the wildwood. In theory, an ecological network functions as a whole, irrespective of the size of the parts, so a network of small woods should interact in a similar way to a single, extensive site. Wildlife should be able to disperse more freely between sites, increasing the chances that habitats and communities will survive the changing climate. Small woodland owners have a major opportunity to contribute to the success of ecological networks through the management of their existing woodland for wildlife, with the possibility of new planting to expand or buffer these woods.

References

Ainsworth, AM, Smith, JH, Boddy, L, Dentinger, BTM, Jordan, M, Parfitt, D, Rogers, HJ and Skeates, SJ. 2013. *Red List of Fungi for Great Britain: Boletaceae; a pilot conservation assessment based on national database records, fruit body morphology and DNA barcoding.* JNCC Species Status 1. JNCC, Peterborough.

Altringham, J. 2003. *British Bats.* The New Naturalist Library. HarperCollins Publishers, London.

Bat Conservation Trust. 2014. *State of the UK's bats 2014. National Bat Monitoring Programme Population Trends.* Bat Conservation Trust, London.

Battersby, J. (ed) and Tracking Mammals Partnership. 2005. *UK Mammals: species, status and population trends. First Report by the Tracking Mammals Partnership.* Joint Nature Conservation Committee, Peterborough/Tracking Mammals Partnership.

Berry, P, Onishi, Y and Paterson, J. 2012. *Understanding the implications of Climate Change for woodland biodiversity and community functioning.* Report for the Forestry Commission.

Blakesley, D and Buckley, GP. 2010. *Woodland creation for wildlife and people in a changing climate: principles and practice.* Pisces Publications, Newbury.

Bright, P, Morris, P and Mitchell-Jones, T. 2006. *The dormouse conservation handbook.* English Nature, Peterborough.

British Trust for Ornithology. 2015. *Managing scrub for nightingales: a BTO guide for land managers and conservation practitioners.* Conservation Advice No. 1. BTO, Thetford.

Buckley, GP and Howell, R. 2004. *The ecological impact of sweet chestnut coppice silviculture on former ancient, broadleaved woodland sites in south-east England.* English Nature Research Reports 627, English Nature, Peterborough.

Buckley, GP and Mills, J. 2015. *The flora and fauna of coppice woods: winners and losers of active management or neglect.* In Kirby, KJ and Watkins, C (eds). *Europe's changing woods and forests: from wildwood to managed landscapes.* CAB International, Oxford. Pp 129–139.

Carey, PD. 2015. *Biodiversity Climate Change impacts report card technical paper 5. Impacts of climate change on terrestrial habitats and vegetation.*

Centre for Hydrology and Ecology. 2010. *Modular Analysis of Vegetation Information (MAVIS).* Lancaster Environment Centre, Lancaster.

Clarke, SA, Green, DG, Bourn, NA and Hoare, DJ. 2011. *Woodland management for butterflies and moths: a best practice guide.* Butterfly Conservation, Wareham.

Collinson, N and Sparks, T. 2008. Phenology – nature's calendar: an overview of results from the UK Phenology Network. *Arboricultural Journal* 30, 271–278.

Davies, C, Fay, N and Mynors, C. 2000. *Veteran trees: A guide to risk and responsibility.* English Nature, Peterborough.

Defra. 2006. *Pesticides: Code of practice for using plant protection products.* Defra, London.

Du Feu, C. 2004. *The BTO nestbox guide.* The British Trust for Ornithology, Thetford.

Du Feu, C. 2005. *Nestboxes.* The British Trust for Ornithology, Thetford.

Eaton, MA, Aebischer, NJ, Brown, AF, Hearn, RD, Lock, L, Musgrove, AJ, Noble, DG, Stroud, DJ and Gregory, RD. 2015. Birds of Conservation Concern 4: the population status of birds in the UK, Channel Islands and Isle of Man. *British Birds* 108, 708–746.

Edgar, P, Foster, J and Baker, J. 2010. *Reptile habitat management handbook.* Amphibian and Reptile Conservation, Bournemouth.

English Nature. 2001. *The upland management handbook.* English Nature, Peterborough

English Nature. 2004. *Reptiles: guidelines for developers.* English Nature, Peterborough.

Evans, J. 1984. *Silviculture of Broadleaved Woodland.* Forestry Commission Bulletin 62. HMSO, London.

Evans, J. and Rolls, W. 2015. *Getting started in your own wood.* Permanent Publications, East Meon.

Evans, S and Kibby, G. 2004. *Fungi.* Dorling Kindersley, London.

Evans, SE, Henrici, A and Ing, B. 2006. *Preliminary assessment: the Red Data List of Threatened British Fungi.* British Mycological Society, Manchester.

Ferris, R and Carter, C. 2000. *Managing rides, roadsides and edge habitats in lowland forests.* Bulletin 123. Forestry Commission, Edinburgh.

Fiegna, C, Dagleish, MP, Coulter, L, Milne, E, Meredith, A, Finlayson, J, Di Nardo, A and McInnes, CJ. 2015. Host-pathogen dynamics of squirrelpox virus infection in red squirrels (*Sciurus vulgaris*). *Veterinary Microbiology* 182, 18–27.

Flower, N. 1980. The management history and structure of unenclosed woods in the New Forest, Hampshire. *Journal of Biogeography* 7, 311–328.

Forestry Commission. 2005. *Woodland management for bats.* Forestry Commission, in partnership with the Bat Conservation Trust, Countryside Council Wales and English Nature.

Forestry Commission. 2008. *English Woodland Grant Scheme: Operations Note 4: National Vegetation Classification.* Forestry Commission England. www.forestry.gov.uk

Forestry Commission. 2011. *Forests and Biodiversity.* UK Forestry Standard Guidelines. Forestry Commission, Edinburgh.

Forestry Commission England. 2010. *Managing ancient and native woodland in England.* Forestry Commission England Practice Guide. Forestry Commission, Bristol.

Forestry Commission Scotland. 2006a. *Forest operations and red squirrels.* FSC Guidance Note 33. http://scotland.forestry.gov.uk/

Forestry Commission Scotland. 2006b. *Seed sources for planting native trees and shrubs in Scotland.* Guidance note. Forestry Commission Scotland, Edinburgh.

Forestry Commission Scotland. 2009. *Management of ancient wood pasture.* Guidance note. Forestry Commission Scotland, Edinburgh.

Forestry Commission Scotland. 2012. *Managing forests as red squirrel strongholds.* Forestry Commission Practice Note 102. Forestry Commission Scotland, Edinburgh.

Forestry Commission and Natural England. 2013. *Guidance on managing woodlands with great crested newts in England.* www.forestry.gov.uk

Forestry Commission Scotland and Scottish Natural Heritage. 2009. *Forest operations and great crested newts in Scotland.* FCS Guidance Note 35b. Forestry Commission Scotland, Edinburgh.

Fox, R, Brereton, TM, Asher, J, August, TA, Botham, MS, Bourn, NAD, Cruickshanks, KL, Bulman, CR, Ellis, S, Harrower, CA, Middlebrook, I, Noble, DG, Powney, GD, Randle, Z, Warren, MS and Roy, DB. 2015. *The State of the UK's Butterflies 2015.* Butterfly Conservation and the Centre for Ecology and Hydrology, Wareham.

Fox, R, Warren, MS and Brereton, TM. 2010. A new Red List of British butterflies. *Species Status* 12, 1–32. Joint Nature Conservation Committee, Peterborough.

Francis, JL, Morton, AJ and Boorman, LA. 1992. The establishment of ground flora species in recently planted woodland. *Aspects of Applied Biology* 29, 171–178.

Gent, T and Gibson, S. 2012. *Herpetofauna Workers Manual.* Pelagic Publishing, Exeter.

Gill, R. 2000. *The impact of deer on woodland biodiversity.* Forestry Commission Information Note 36. Forestry Commission, Edinburgh.

Gurnell, J, Lurz, P, McDonald, R and Pepper, H. 2009. *Practical techniques for surveying and monitoring squirrels.* Forestry Commission Practice Note 11. Forestry Commission, Farnham.

Hall, JE, Kirby, KJ and Whitbread, AM. 2004. *National Vegetation Classification: Field guide to woodland.* Joint Nature Conservation Committee, Peterborough.

Harmer, R. 2004. *Restoration of neglected coppice.* Forest Information Note 56. Forestry Commission, Edinburgh.

Harmer, R and Howe, J. 2003. *The silviculture and management of coppice woodlands.* Forestry Commission, Edinburgh.

Harris, E. 2009. Blowing the cover. *Smallwoods* 2009, 10–13.

Harris, S, Morris, P, Wray, S and Yalden, DW. 1995. *A review of British Mammals: population estimates and conservation status of British mammals other than cetaceans.* Joint Nature Conservation Committee, Peterborough.

Hart, C. 1995. *Alternative silvicultural systems to clear-cutting in Britain: a review.* Forestry Commission Bulletin 115. HMSO, London.

Hayhow, DB, Bond AL, Eaton MA, Grice PV, Hall C, Hall J, Harris SJ, Hearn RD, Holt CA, Noble DG, Stroud DA and Wotton S. 2015. *The state of the UK's birds 2015.* RSPB, BTO, WWT, JNCC, NE, NIEA, NRW and SNH, Sandy.

Herbert, R, Samuel, S and Patterson, G. 1999. *Using local stock for planting native trees and shrubs.* Forestry Commission Practice Note 8. Forestry Commission, Edinburgh.

Highways Agency. 2005. *The establishment of an herbaceous plant layer in roadside woodland.* Design manual for roads and bridges. Volume 10, Section 3, Part 3. Highways Agency. The Stationery Office, Norwich.

Hill, MO. 1996. *TABLEFIT Version 1.0, For Identification of Vegetation Types.* Institute of Terrestrial Ecology, Huntingdon.

Hill, DA and Greenaway, F. 2008. Conservation of bats in British woodlands. *British Wildlife* 19, 161–169.

Hodder, KH and Bullock, JM. 2009. Really wild? Naturalistic grazing in modern landscapes. *British Wildlife* 20, 37–43.

Hodge, SJ and Peterken, GF. 1998. Deadwood in British forests: priorities and a strategy. *Forestry* 71, 99–112.

Holl, K. and Smith, M. 2002. *Ancient Wood pasture in Scotland: Classification and management principles.*

Scottish Natural Heritage Commissioned Report F01AA108.

Holt, CA, Fuller, RJ and Dolman, PM. 2010. Experimental evidence that deer browsing reduces habitat suitability for breeding Common Nightingales *Luscinia megarhynchos. Ibis* 152, 335–346.

Holt, CA, Fuller, RJ and Dolman, PM. 2011. Breeding and post-breeding responses of woodland birds to modification of habitat structure by deer. *Biological Conservation* 144, 2151–2162.

Hopkins, J. 2007. British wildlife and climate change 2. Adapting to climate change. *British Wildlife* 18, 381–387.

Hoppit, A. 2014. *Handling oak in OPM areas.* Forestry Commission England. www.forestry.gov.uk/pdf/ Good_practice_guide_Handling_OPM_ material_04-2014.pdf/

Hubert, J and Cundall, E. 2006. *Choosing provenance in broadleaved trees.* Forestry Commission Information Note 82. Forestry Commission Scotland, Edinburgh.

Humphrey, J and Bailey, S. 2012. *Managing deadwood in forests and woodlands.* Forestry Commission Practice Guide. Forestry Commission, Edinburgh.

Humphrey, J, Stevenson, A, Whitfield, P and Swailes, J. 2002. *Life in the deadwood: a guide to managing deadwood in Forestry Commission forests.* Forestry Commission, Edinburgh.

Humphrey, JW, Ferris, F and Quine, CP. 2003. *Biodiversity in Britain's planted forests.* Forestry Commission, Edinburgh.

Hundt, L. 2012. *Bat surveys: good practice guidelines*, 2nd edition. Bat Conservation Trust, London.

Ingwood, H, Fleming, A, Pungetti, G, Makhzoumi, J, Rackham, O, Jongman, R and Selman, P. 2015. *Econets, landscape & people: integrating people's values and cultural services into the design of ecological networks and other landscape change proposals.* Natural England Commissioned Report, Number 180.

Institute of Environmental Assessment. 1995. *Guidelines for baseline ecological assessment.* Institute of Environmental Assessment. E & F Spon, An imprint of Chapman & Hall, London.

Joint Nature Conservation Committee. 2006. *National Vegetation Classification users' handbook.* JNCC, Peterborough.

Kallow, S. 2014. *UK National Tree Seed Project Seed Collecting Manual.* Royal Botanic Gardens Kew, Richmond.

Kennedy, CEJ and Southwood, TRE. 1984. The number of insects associated with British trees: a re-analysis. *Journal of Animal Ecology* 53, 455–478.

Kerr, G. 2008. *Managing continuous cover forests.* Operational Guidance Booklet 7 *(OGB7).* Forestry Commission, Edinburgh.

Langton, T, Beckett, C, Foster, J. 2001. Great Crested Newt Conservation Handbook. Froglife, Halesworth. www.froglife.org/wp-content/uploads/2013/06/GCN-Conservation-Handbook_compressed.pdf

Lawton, JH, Brotherton, PNM, Brown, VK, Elphick, C, Fitter, AH, Forshaw, J, Haddow, RW, Hilborne, S, Leafe, RN, Mace, GM, Southgate, MP, Sutherland, WA, Tew, TE, Varley, J and Wynne, GR. 2010. *Making Space for Nature: a review of England's wildlife sites and ecological network.* Report to Defra. Defra, London.

Lewington, R. 2015. *Pocket Guide to the Butterflies of Great Britain and Ireland.* British Wildlife Publishing, Gillingham.

Lonsdale, D. 2000. *Hazards from trees: a general guide.* Forestry Commission Practice Guide. Forestry Commission, Edinburgh.

Lonsdale, D (ed). 2013. *Ancient and other veteran trees: further guidance on management.* The Tree Council, London.

Mayle, B. 1999. *Domestic stock grazing to enhance woodland biodiversity.* Forestry Commission Information Note 28. Forestry Commission, Edinburgh.

Mayle, B, Ferryman, M and Pepper, H. 2007. *Controlling grey squirrel damage to woodlands.* Forestry Commission Practice Note 4. Forestry Commission, Edinburgh.

Mitchell, FJC and Kirby, KJ. 1990. The impact of large herbivores on the conservation of semi-natural woods in British Uplands. *Forestry* 63, 333–353.

Mitchell, PL. 1989. Repollarding large neglected pollards: A review of current practice and results. *Arboricultural Journal* 13, 125–142.

Morecroft, MD and Speakman, L. 2015. *Biodiversity climate change impacts summary report. Living With Environmental Change Network.* www.nerc.ac.uk/research/partnerships/lwec/products/report-cards/biodiversity/report-card/

Morrison, CA and Robinson, RA. 2015. *Biodiversity Climate Change impacts report card technical paper 11. The impact of climate change on migration.*

National Tree Safety Group. 2011. *Common sense risk management of trees.* Forestry Commission, Edinburgh.

Natural England. 2008. *Bracken management and control.* Natural England Technical Information Note TIN048. Natural England, Peterborough.

Oliver, T, Marshall, H, Huntingford, C, Prudhomme, C, Pearce-Higgins, C, Martay, B, Crowe, A, Duffield, SA and Morecroft, MD. 2015. *The role of landscape and site scale characteristics in making species populations resilient to climate change and extreme events.* Natural England Commissioned Report, Number 149.

Parsons, MS and Greatorex-Davies, N. 2006. The value of Sweet Chestnut *Castanea sativa* as a foodplant for Lepidoptera. *Entomologist's Record and Journal of Variation* 118, 1–11.

Peterken, GF. 1996. *Natural woodland: ecology and conservation in north temperate regions.* Cambridge University Press, Cambridge.

Peterken, GF. 2001. Ecological effects of introduced tree species in Britain. *Forest Ecology and Management* 141, 31–42.

Plantlife. 2003. *Bluebells for Britain: A report on the 2003 Bluebells for Britain survey.* Plantlife, Salisbury.

Putman, R. 1986. *Grazing in temperate forest ecosystems: large herbivores and the ecology of the New Forest.* Croom Helm, London.

Rackham, O. 1990. *Trees and woodland in the British landscape.* Dent, London.

Rackham, O. 2003. *Ancient Woodland its history, vegetation and uses in England.* New edition. Castlepoint Press, Scotland.

Read, HJ. 2000. *Veteran trees: a guide to good management.* English Nature, Peterborough.

Roberts, P and Ovenden, D. 2003.*Guide to the Reptiles and Amphibians of Britain and Ireland.* Field Studies Council, Shrewsbury.

Rodwell, JS. (ed) (1991 *et seq.*) *British Plant Communities,* volume 1 (*Woodlands and Scrub* (1991)); volume 2 (*Heaths and Mires* (1991)); volume 3 (*Grasslands and Montane Communities* (1992)); Volume 4 (*Aquatic Communities, Swamps and Tall-herb Fens* (1995)); volume 5 (*Maritime and Weed Communities and Vegetation of Open Habitats* (2000)). Cambridge University Press, Cambridge.

Rose, F. 2006. *The Wildflower Key.* Penguin Books, England.

Savill, PS, Thompson, FB and Waters, TL. 1997. *Ecology of sycamore in Britain. How does it compete with native trees?* In Ratcliffe, PR (ed). *Native and non-native in British forestry.* Institute of Chartered Foresters, Edinburgh. Pp 57–68.

SEARS. 2008. *Bracken control: a guide to best practice.* Natural Scotland.

Smithers, R and Sparks, T. 2010. 'Climate is what we expect, weather is what we get'. *British Wildlife* 21, 236–239.

Sparks, T and Crick, H. 2015. *Biodiversity Climate Change impacts report card technical paper. 12. The impact of climate change on biological phenology in the UK.* Living With Environmental Change.

Spooner, B and Roberts, P. 2005. *Fungi.* The New Naturalist Library. HarperCollins Publishers, London.

Stebbings, RE and Walsh, ST. 1991. *Bat boxes.* The Bat Conservation Trust, London.

Sterry, P and Hughes, B. 2009. *Collins complete guide to British mushrooms and toadstools.* HarperCollins Publishers, London.

Sumsion, L and Pollock, M. 2005. *Woodland grazing toolkit.* Argyll and Bute Local Biodiversity Partnership.

Svensson, L, Mullarney, K and Zetterström, D. 2010. *Collins bird guide 2nd edition.* HarperCollins Publishers, London.

Swanson, G, Armstrong, H and Campbell, D. 2008. *Estimating deer abundance in woodlands: the combination plot technique.* Forestry Commission Bulletin 128. Forestry Commission, Edinburgh.

Symes, N and Currie, F. 2005. *Woodland management for birds: a guide to managing for declining woodland birds in England.* The RSPB, Sandy and Forestry Commission, Peterborough.

Thompson R, Humphrey J, Harmer, R and Ferris, R. 2003. *Restoration of native woodland on ancient woodland sites.* Forest Commission Practice Guide. Forestry Commission, Edinburgh.

Troup, RS. 1928. *Silvicultural systems.* Clarendon Press, Oxford.

UKWAS. 2012. *The UK Woodland Assurance Standard Third Edition* (version 3.1). UKWAS, Edinburgh.

Vera, FWM. 2000. *Grazing Ecology and Forest History.* CABI Publishing, UK.

Visitor Safety in the Countryside Group. 2011. *Managing visitor safety in the countryside: principles and practice.* York Publishing Services, York.

Walmsley, CA, Smithers, RJ, Berry, PM, Harley, M, Stevenson, MJ and Catchpole, R. 2007. *Monarch (Modelling Natural resources to Climate Change): a synthesis for biodiversity conservation.* UKCIP, Oxford.

Wildlife Trusts. 2007. *Living landscapes. A call to restore the UK's battered ecosystems, for wildlife and people.* The Wildlife Trusts, UK.

Williams, P, Biggs, J, Whitfield, M, Thorne, A, Bryant, S, Fox, G and Nicolet, P. 2010. *The Pond Book: a guide to the management and creation of ponds.* Pond Conservation Trust, Oxford Brookes.

Willoughby, I, Evans, H, Gibbs, J, Pepper, H, Gregory, S, Dewar, J, Nisbet, T, Pratt, J, McKay, H, Siddons, R, Mayle, B, Heritage, S, Ferris, R and Trout, R. 2004. *Reducing pesticide use in forestry.* Forestry Commission Practice Guide. Forestry Commission, Edinburgh.

Woodland Trust. 2005. *The conservation and restoration of plantations on ancient woodland sites: a guide for woodland owners and managers.* www.woodlandtrust.org.uk

Yalden, D. 1999. *The history of British mammals.* T. & A.D. Poyser, London.